CW00739499

THE
MONKEY
GLAND
AFFAIR

THE MONKEY GLAND AFFAIR

DAVID
HAMILTON

CHATTO & WINDUS
LONDON

Published in 1986 by
Chatto & Windus Ltd
40 William IV Street
London WC2N 4DF

All rights reserved. No part
of this publication may be reproduced,
stored in a retrieval system, or
transmitted in any form, or by
any means, electronic, mechanical,
photocopying or otherwise, without
the prior permission of the
publisher.

British Library Cataloguing in Publication Data

Hamilton, David, *1939–*
The monkey gland affair.
1. Voronoff, Serge   2. Medical scientists
—Biography
I. Title
617′.46   RC870.92.V6/

ISBN 0-7011-3021-0

Copyright © David Hamilton 1986

Designed by Humphrey Stone
Printed in Great Britain by
Redwood Burn Ltd.,
Trowbridge, Wiltshire

I dedicate this book to

SERGE-SAMUEL VORONOFF

*who, I believe, has taken undue blame for the
excesses of the gland transplant era.
I admire his enthusiasm and persistence: moreover,
he was not the first, nor the last,
scientist to deceive himself.*

CONTENTS

ILLUSTRATIONS

between pages 78 and 91

INTRODUCTION

While working on a history of organ transplantation, it became clear
to me that conventional accounts of the subject usually omitted some
of the activities of the early twentieth century – such as the widespread but mistaken claims that skin grafts taken from one person
could be grafted to another. But there is another even more important omission: the activities of the testicle gland transplanters of the
1920s are seldom recorded at all.

At first sight, the exclusion of this 'monkey gland affair' and
similar rejuvenation methods seems entirely proper. Quackery has
no place in histories of the main stream of surgical progress, and an
aberration which made a good music hall joke can hardly be taken
seriously by historians.

But further study shows that the gland-grafters and their operations are more interesting than might be thought. The surgeons who
were prominently involved, and are now ridiculed, were not alone.
Throughout the 1920s, many respectable medical men and scientists
believed (wrongly) that tissue taken from animals could survive and
function after being transplanted into human beings without the use
of drugs to prevent rejection. Even today, such drugs are needed to
prevent the rejection of grafts from one person to another; nor are
they yet powerful enough to prevent the rejection of transplants from
animals to man. During the 1920s a surprising number of surgeons
carried out testicle transplants to rejuvenate their ageing male
patients. One of these, 'Dr' John R. Brinkley, was certainly a quack,
but the career of the best known of the monkey gland transplanters –
Serge Voronoff – was more orthodox than is now supposed. He had
conventional early medical appointments, and wrote on orthodox
themes; it could not be said that he was simply interested in money,
since he was independently wealthy; he was not the pioneer of testis

transplantation, since others preceded him; and he could claim plausibly that his surgery was based on the orthodox science of the day. For a while, in the 1920s, he was highly regarded: in France his work was supported by the government and by his medical and veterinary colleagues.

The erroneous beliefs of Voronoff and others were slowly eliminated in the 1930s and 1940s. It was realised that attempts to transplant tissue from animals to man or even from one human being to another were doomed to failure without the use of drugs. An episode of poor science was forgotten, and gland transplants became ridiculed. Conventional medical men conveniently failed to remember that they had ever believed in it, and in Serge Voronoff there was a convenient scapegoat to take all the opprobrium for a decade of error. His direct appeal to the public and to journalists, which had made him conspicuous and famous in the 1920s, left him to take the blame for this aberration of medical science, a symptom of the frivolity of the 1920s.

This book is about a major deviation from the mainstream of medical progress, but I hope it also sheds some light on the uses and misuses of 'the scientific method'. It is usual to investigate the progress of science by examining the lives and works of successful pioneers: perhaps a close look at the disastrous efforts of a man like Voronoff may also obliquely illuminate the ways in which new ideas are born.

It is not necessary to know much about medical science to understand this book. Only two concepts have to be mastered. The first is that the glands of the body – for example, the testis, adrenal and thyroid – make and liberate substances into the blood which affect the workings of the rest of the body. These glands are called the *endocrine* glands, and the substances secreted, which can be extracted from the glands, are called *hormones*. The second principle to recall is that tissue taken from one person and grafted to another is almost invariably rejected. The few exceptions to this rule are special cases, such as cornea grafts, to which blood vessels never reach, and bone, which serves as an inert implant. Grafts taken from animals and transplanted to man are very rapidly rejected. Second grafts from humans or animals are rejected even more quickly than first ones.

This book describes a time in the 1920s when these simple biological rules had not been established firmly. Very little was known of the endocrine glands, and almost nothing about transplants. As a result, it was possible for some scientists and medical men to claim that grafts of glands from human to human, or from animals to man, might succeed, and thus replace real or imaginary deficiencies in the patient's own glands. It was this uncertainty which encouraged gland-grafting.

The lives of scientists and medical men often make dull reading. There are exceptions, and transplantation produced men who, like some transplanters of today, enjoyed the full glare of publicity. Certainly, there was nothing dull about the gland transplanters of the 1920s.

DAVID HAMILTON
Glasgow 1986

ACKNOWLEDGEMENTS

It is a pleasure to thank those who took an interest in this project, and who gave of their time to help complete it.

Jean Robertson read the manuscript, and she and her staff in the Reference section of Glasgow University Library traced much obscure bibliographical and biographical material.

Dr H. A. Copeman, Department of Medicine, University of Western Australia, Perth, introduced me to Mrs Elizabeth Leighton-Jones, who was Voronoff's secretary in the late 1920s. Her daughter, Elisabeth, of Paris, translated and commented on Voronoff's letters.

Mr John Pitt, Acting General Secretary of the British Union for the Abolition of Vivisection, discovered the many references to Voronoff in the journal *The Abolitionist*.

Mrs Ann Williamson, Assistant Secretary to the Thoroughbred Breeders Association, found details of their debate on gland-grafting and provided biographical information on the participants.

Mr N.A.M. Rodger of the Public Records Office, London, found the government file on Voronoff, and Mr John Westmancoat and the staff of the British Library Newspaper Library at Colindale advised me during my initial searches for information.

Mrs Mary Watkins of the Reference/Local History Library in Gary, Indiana obtained details of the Rugh affair.

Mr M. K. Madding, Public Information Officer, California State Prison, San Quentin, obtained biographical details on Dr. L. L. Stanley.

Patrick Ryan of the Library of St George's Hospital Medical School, London, traced the career of Ivor Back, while Eustace H. Cornelius, librarian of the Royal College of Surgeons of England, provided the list of Hunterian lecturers.

The Librarians of the Alexis Carrel Collection, Georgetown University, Washington D.C. allowed access to the letters between Veronoff and Carrel.

John R. Woodard of Z. Smith Reynolds Library, Wake Forest University, North Carolina provided details of the Bostwick legacy.

Patricia A. Michaelis, Curator of Manuscripts, Kansas State Historical Society, Topeka, Kansas guided me through the Brinkley papers and other local sources. The Historical Society kindly gave permission to publish their photographs of Brinkley.

Dr H. A. Bruck of Penicuik gave me information on the Pontifical Academy of Sciences.

The writing of this book was assisted by Dr Counihan and the PARC hospital management, Dublin and Baghdad. The Fellowship at the Wellcome Unit for the History of Medicine at Oxford University.

My thanks also go to Grace Anderson and Irene Black who typed the manuscript with enthusiasm.

Lastly I thank Andrew Bradley and Jean my wife who both agreed that this book should be written: and Jeremy Lewis of Chatto & Windus, who agreed that it should be published, and made many helpful comments.

I

VORONOFF:
THE EARLY YEARS

In about the year 1919, the middle-aged French surgeon Serge Voronoff determined to seek for himself a place in the history of medical science. Encouraged by some results from experiments in animals, he felt confident enough to try his surgical operation on human patients. This consisted of the transplantation of grafts of monkey testicles into ageing men, and he hoped to achieve rejuvenation – a reversal of the declining medical and physical powers in old age.

By the middle of the 1920s he had established an international reputation as a pioneer of a controversial kind. He had support from many orthodox medical men and his surgical *méthode* was widely copied. He had a huge income from performing the operation on patients from all parts of the world and his comings and goings were always news.

But by the time of his death he was increasingly thought of as a quack, and he and his monkey gland operations were not only discredited but had become part of the language, so much so that mention of the need for a 'monkey gland operation' was more than likely to excite disrespectful and derisive mirth.

I

The man who came to be regarded as the pioneer of gland-grafting was born in Russia in 1866, the son of a vodka manufacturer in Voronège. Little is known of his early life. He attended school there and, at the age of eighteen, moved to Paris, studying first classics, then medicine. He graduated in 1893, becoming assistant to the Paris surgeon Pean. Three of his brothers also came to France, while one remained behind in Russia. He became a French citizen in 1895, and such was his cultural assimilation that it was often said later that he had become more French than the French.

From Paris, the young man travelled to Egypt, which was then under French influence. He had been recommended by his teachers for the post of personal physician to the Court of the ruler, Khedive Abbas II – a title of which Voronoff was proud, and continued to use later on his visiting card. During this time, he wrote standard works on surgery and gynaecology, and published an account of his surgical experience with liver abscesses. He set up a nurses' training school and organised a successful conference on tropical medicine in Cairo. He also started a new medical society there and launched a journal devoted to tropical medicine, *La Presse Médicale d'Egypte*. In Egypt, he married the daughter of Ferdinand de Lesseps, and in 1902 the couple were prominent in the celebrations of the opening of the Suez Canal. In about 1910 they returned to Paris, after which we know much more of his scientific and medical career.

It seems that he became a fashionable medical man, well-known in Paris, and is depicted as such in the gossipy Paris magazine *Chanteclair* of 1911. First-hand accounts of him describe his considerable charm and dignity. He wrote well and lectured in convincing style. He was six feet two inches tall, and this stature must have added to his already considerable presence. In autobiographical entries, he listed golf as his sport, but he spent little time on the links. He loved the theatre, and the great wealth he was later to accumulate enabled him to collect art treasures. Later he became friendly with well-known contemporaries such as Sarah Bernhardt, Maurice Maeterlinck, Arthur Nikisch and Monet, and he was known to the royal families of Europe. He apparently spoke poor English; later, during his lectures abroad, a translation was given by his wife, his secretary or an assistant, which added to the impact on his audience.

II

Until 1910, when he was forty-four years old, Voronoff had shown no evidence of interest in what was to be his *forte* – tissue transplantation. It seems that his work until then had been devoted entirely to private surgical practice and to the struggle to establish his reputation. He had no salaried post in any institution. His expertise had been broadened by his experience of tropical medicine and surgery in Egypt, and he may have acquired considerable skills. His had been an entirely conventional career.

When he turned to research in middle age, tissue transplantation was a not unreasonable choice of project. There had been a good deal of pioneering interest and progress in the subject from the turn of the century until the start of the First World War. It was a time of broad advance in many aspects of surgery resulting from the refinement of antiseptic and aseptic methods.

The transplantation of tissue has a long history. In ancient India, flaps of skin were transplanted from the forehead to the nose, and these operations were refined by Tagliacozzi and published in his famous book in the Middle Ages. John Hunter attempted testicle transplants in the eighteenth century, and wrongly claimed some success. In the nineteenth century, success with free skin grafts was achieved when it was realised that if the skin was very thin it could be detached completely and used as a graft. Transplants of many types were attempted experimentally in animals and in man. Grafts were usually made using simple implants of slices or blocks of tissue – of skin, bone or glands for example – into which new blood vessels grew: these were then rejected. A great advance in the transplantation of organs was achieved by linking the blood vessels of the organ and the recipient; the artery and vein of the graft were joined to an artery and vein in the recipient, so connecting it immediately to the recipient's circulation. These attempts at organ transplantation were a direct result of the first successful means of joining blood vessels, which was devised by an Austrian called Edward Payr. His method, which was soon discarded, involved a magnesium ring similar in size to the blood vessels that were to be joined: he drew the vessels over the ring and tied them together over it. Using Payr's method, the first experimental kidney transplant ever to be performed was carried out in 1902 by Emerich Ullmann in Vienna, when the city was at the height of its medical fame. The kidney was taken from one dog and transplanted to another. The transplanted kidney produced urine for a few days but the flow ceased when the kidney was rejected. This experiment caused considerable interest in

Vienna at the time, and was described on the front page of its medical journal.

This method of joining blood vessels was cumbersome, and failure was frequent. Experiments with other methods which did not involve the rings or other stents continued. In France, Professor Mathieu Jaboulay of Lyons, the head of an active surgical unit, published an alternative, simpler method for joining blood vessels, similar to that now universally used, whereby the blood vessels were simply stitched together with an encircling of sutures. Another surgeon working in Lyons was, however, to get the credit for adding the final improvements to Jaboulay's method and inventing the method of joining blood vessels which has been used ever since. This surgeon was Alexis Carrel, then a young man, who later achieved a world-wide fame. His method was only slightly different from Jaboulay's, emphasising as he did the need for fine, lubricated needles and thread. An ambitious, solitary worker, Carrel was at odds with the senior surgeons in Lyons, and his failure to give credit to Jaboulay and others in Lyons for their earlier work may have added to his reputation for awkwardness. Jaboulay had been the first to attempt a kidney transplant in a human patient: the two patients involved were suffering from chronic renal failure, and Jaboulay used kidneys taken from a pig in one case and a goat in the other.

These transplants failed immediately. Carrel failed to obtain promotion in Lyons, and left for North America. His rebuff led him to denigrate French medical science in later years; in fact European surgery before the First World War was impressive, and the German and French surgical clinics were well organised along lines which were successfully copied by the many visitors from North America. Carrel settled in Chicago, where he worked with the physiologist, C. Guthrie. Together they published an astonishing series of organ transplants in animals. These included successful removal and re-implantation into the same animal of the animal's own kidney and heart. They tried to transplant organs from one animal to another, but these only functioned for a short time. They also transplanted blood vessels. Guthrie's modification of Carrel's method and his skill may have been decisive in these famous experiments. Predictably, Guthrie became irritated at Carrel's attitudes and personal ambition, and the two quarrelled. By this time Carrel had obtained promotion and was in charge of surgical research at the Rockefeller Institute, New York, an appointment which lent distinction to the new Institute.

III

In 1910, Voronoff started experimental work on organ transplantation. There was a great deal of interest in the subject at the time, resulting from the discovery of successful methods of joining blood vessels together, while Lister's methods of antisepsis were not only successful in human surgery but made it possible for experimental animal surgery to succeed as well; moreover, Alexis Carrel had become famous as a result of his transplantation work, and no doubt Voronoff wished to copy him. Carrel's personal papers contain a number of friendly letters from Voronoff which suggest that the two were known to each other, and Voronoff describes to Carrel the difficulties he was having in getting experiments on transplantation under way.

On 20 January Voronoff wrote as follows:

Dear Friend,
    . . . I read the very interesting paper given in your name by Pozzi at the Academy of Medicine and was naturally very pleased.

    For my part, I am able to announce good news. I have begun working. I sometimes operate at night – at present I am very busy during the day – and on Sunday mornings.

    But in general I am rather dissatisfied with dogs for the research I am conducting. The anatomical arrangement of the genital organs is not very suitable for these experiments – the cornua of the uterus are very long and lead directly to the ovary which complicates the operation since it means that the grafted cornu must be sutured, and its 'vitality' is problematical.

    I am therefore considering using other animals. Yesterday at the abattoir I studied the anatomy of the genital organs of the ewe. The arrangement is not at all the same as that of the dog, and is much closer to that of the human.

    Grafting would therefore be much easier. But the ovarian vessels are numerous and very small. Suture would not be possible and consequently there would be the fear that the ovary grafted under these conditions would end up atrophied.

I am going to continue my research in this direction on other animals and shall keep you informed.

My house will soon be transformed into Noah's Ark, but I presume that venerable patriarch had more rustic and less refined tastes than the present generation, since my wife and I are beginning to feel a certain indisposition among all these animals.

I have already wished you a thousand good things for the New Year in a post card sent to New York, but I fear you have not received it since you are now in France. I repeat them from the heart, wishing you every happiness and shaking your hand affectionately.

Yours,
Voronoff

Two years later, in 1912, Carrel was awarded a Nobel Prize for his pioneer work in devising methods of organ transplantation, though he had not done any gland transplants. Voronoff was quick to congratulate him on his award: 'Heureux pour vous: embrasse fraternellement,' he cabled from Paris on 11 October 1912. Carrel's replies to Voronoff were encouraging and cordial, but not effusive. They contain his well-known criticisms of the state of French science, and hinted that Voronoff would need to give up private surgical practice if he wanted to succeed in research. The letters again suggest that the two men had met: Voronoff later claimed to have worked with Carrel at the Rockefeller Institute, a claim which the Rockefeller administration had to deny. Voronoff's work at this time, judging by his letters to Carrel, was on ovary grafting, not on the testis transplants which were to make him famous after the First World War: he was trying to transplant whole ovaries, in an attempt to devise a cure for infertility.

But although Voronoff had taken up transplantation research at a time of international interest in this type of surgery, there was still much confusion about tissue transplantation. Despite widespread interest in the subject, and numerous attempts at the transplantation of many types of tissue, erroneous claims were still being made to the effect that grafts from one person to another might succeed. This uncertainty is puzzling to later generations, who know that rejection is the rule. There are a good many reasons for this misunderstanding. Perhaps the authority of John Hunter, the great experimentalist, who claimed success with ovary grafting in the eighteenth century, gave credence to the idea of successful grafting; grafting between different types of plants, notably shrubs and fruit trees, was successful. There were certain cases of undoubted success in the human species with grafts of cornea or bone – both of which are now known to be special cases and to survive because the cornea needs no new blood vessels to grow in, while in the case of bone only the graft's strong inert skeleton, and not the cells, need survive.

Further confusion was caused by endless claims that skin grafts from unrelated human donors would 'take'. Human skin was often grafted onto those patients needing a graft, such as a victim of burns. The reasons for such claims are unclear, since the grafts must all have eventually rejected after healing in for a matter of days only. Perhaps the surgeons in the early years of the century thought that for the graft to have taken for a week or so meant success, and that its subsequent loss was either bad luck or the fault of others. In other cases, rejection of the graft left a scab, which can mimic a surviving graft: sometimes the patient's own skin grew back under the scab, revealing an apparently successful graft beneath when the scab fell off.

This confusion also meant that tissue from animals might be used to graft into humans. Animal skin of many types was used for skin-grafting. As we have seen, Professor Jaboulay of Lyons had, in 1906, tried to transplant animal kidneys into human patients. He was a skilled, experienced and respected surgical scientist, and his use of animal kidneys was not a bizarre or controversial choice: it was consistent with the erroneous assumptions of the day that grafts between species could succeed. It did not contradict any known laws of transplantation at that time, for there were none.

Whatever the cause, the effect of this confused situation was that all sorts of claims were made for tissue transplantation, and grandiose plans drawn up – including Voronoff's scheme for animal experiments involving the transplanting of ovaries. Doubtless he had in mind a subsequent plan to cure infertility in women. To Voronoff in 1912, transplantation must have seemed an exciting new field: and within a short time he was to have an opportunity to transplant a thyroid gland into a human patient, and do bone-grafting on a considerable scale.

In the midst of this confusion, one person had a correct view of transplantation. Carrel was in no doubt that grafts from one member of the same species to another, or to a distant species, would fail. This conclusion was widely ignored, perhaps in the hope that he was wrong, or perhaps because he had stopped transplanting by 1912, and had turned to tissue culture. Ironically, the many testimonials to him at the time of his Nobel Prize ignored his caution about transplantation and suggested that success with such transplantation had been achieved, or was not far away. The *New York Times*, excited by the news of the first Nobel Prize to go to America, commented in 1912 in a euphoric editorial that Carrel had 'not only succeeded in transplanting the organs of animals . . . but has cut them out and grown them to monstrous size . . . the artificial grown tissues had been used with measurable success to replace diseased and worn out tissues.'

The public were in no mood for caution, and it was to surgeons and surgery they looked for success. Some surgeons were to provide good news.

IV

Carrel and Voronoff were brought closer together by the 1914–18 war in Europe. Both surgeons joined the French army. Carrel was on holiday in France when hostilities broke out. As a French citizen, he volunteered – or was drafted – to serve as a medical officer, and was given positions in army hospitals first at Lyons, and then at Compiègne, forty miles north-east of Paris. He was then at the height of his intellectual powers, and within a short time the Rockefeller Institute in New York had backed his war work in Europe and gave money for war injuries research. At the beginning of the war at least, the newspapers continued to follow Carrel attentively, and to describe his successes. After his award of the Nobel Prize, his life and his work were always news, and it is clear that he was helpful to newsmen looking for a story. He understood their methods and needs, and was always ready with news of a new research breakthrough and of his future plans. After he joined the army, stories about him appeared regularly from the Paris correspondent of the *New York Times*.

It was this same correspondent who, in 1914, wrote up a piece on Voronoff. It was the first of the Russian surgeon's many appearances in the newspapers.

July 1st, Paris.
Dr Voronoff, a well-known surgeon, cured a cretin by grafting the thyroid gland of a monkey to a child of fourteen. This resulted in immediate growth. Members of the Academy (French Academy of Sciences) considered the operation of great importance and tending to confirm the great possibilities of constructive surgery as introduced by Dr Alexis Carrel of New York.

Perhaps Voronoff himself decided to issue a press release about his medical research in much the same way as Carrel did, or perhaps the *New York Times* correspondent had sought him out and encouraged him; but while Carrel managed to evade the perils of such exposure, Voronoff's reputation was eventually to be destroyed by it.

The thyroid-grafted patient mentioned in the news item was the son of a chief clerk at the French War Office. The photographs of the patient before the surgery do not suggest a completely cretinous state, and hence, particularly in this pubertal period, spontaneous improvement was possible, which accounts for claims that the monkey thyroid graft had succeeded. Certainly the boy was taken into the navy two years later at the age of seventeen. Voronoff used this story repeatedly in later publications, and the rather unconvincing 'before and after' photographs of the lad frequently appear in his books.

Voronoff had by this time been called up for service in the French army, and was at first given a post at the Russian Hospital in Bordeaux. Here he operated on patients requiring bone-grafting as a result of war wounds which had fragmented the bones of their arms or legs. He seems to have been successful, and his work was admired. He used the patient's own bone, and also animal bone 'as a temporary scaffold'. A second news item on Voronoff's wartime activities appeared shortly afterwards in the same year:

Special cable to *The New York Times*.
PARIS December 4th. The Russian surgeon, Dr Serge Voronoff, who with Dr Alexis Carrel discovered the method of bone-grafting at the Rockefeller Institute, today announced the first successful application of the method in the case of a wounded soldier at the Russian Hospital in

Bordeaux . . . Monkey bone will now be used exclusively for this class of work and Dr Troussaunt, Head of the Army Medical Service, will assist in the development.

Doubtless, Voronoff himself allowed this press release to go out, and, as in the previous story, Voronoff linked his work closely to that of Carrel.

The claims in the story about bone-grafting, however, were quite dishonest. Bone-grafting was not new: among others, William Macewen had used it in Glasgow from 1881 onwards, and Voronoff knew this well. But it was characteristic of Voronoff to simplify a scientific story in this manner, and later he was to be severely criticised for such discourtesy.

There was further news about Carrel in early 1915, but between then and 1919 he and Voronoff virtually disappeared from the newspapers. Such silence was enforced rather than voluntary. Both men were now employed by the French military authorities, and it was customary in wartime to insist on strict secrecy about methods of medical management and research, even in scientific journals, on the grounds that new medical methods can be of assistance to the enemy. Carrel and Voronoff were temporarily muzzled.

II
THE SEARCH FOR
YOUTH

In March 1915, Voronoff moved from his post as chief surgeon to the Russian Hospital. The tributes to him on this occasion were warm-hearted and sincere. He moved to a similar post with the Paris military hospital run by l'Union des Femmes de France. A year later he developed an abscess in his arm and, in spite of an operation at his own hospital, he developed complications, and required further surgery for abscesses of the lungs and liver. Not surprisingly, he left the army in 1917 and returned to civilian medical work. About this time, for reasons which are not clear, he divorced his wife. They had no family, and remained on good terms thereafter.

Voronoff was not intent on extending his research interests, and made a determined and successful bid to obtain a place in an eminent institution. His old teacher, Professor Bouchard, recommended him to the government-run Collège de France and, after vigorous lobbying by both men, a place was made available in the department of Professor Gley. Voronoff's admission was undoubtedly helped by his offer to pay for the unit personally, which also gave him complete freedom within the department and a highly respectable affiliation. He endowed the laboratory by gifting to it the revenue from a substantial holding of Standard Oil Shares. This appointment, made by the personal decision of a government minister, was *aut vitam aut culpam*, which in Voronoff's case was doubly significant.

Voronoff's official title was 'Directeur-adjoint' of the Biological Laboratory of l'École Pratique des Haute Études, and later Director of the Physiological Station at the Collège de France – Foundation Voronoff. The last two words were quickly dropped. This was not a professorial appointment: the title 'Professor' was given to him later by the newspapers. The Collège had a tradition of being liberal and innovative and many compared it favourably with its conservative rival, the Faculté de Médecine of the Sorbonne. Voronoff's name could now be linked with previous medical men of the Collège – men of distinction such as Laennec, Magendie, Claude Bernard and, as mentioned below, Charles Brown-Séquard.

Voronoff was by then fifty-three years old – hardly a promising age for a move into research and for a major new project. He did not return to ovary-grafting and his first reports show a brief flirtation with attempts to accelerate wound healing with hormone powder, which closely followed an erroneous similar claim by Carrel. But from then on his research work, which was to make him famous and then notorious, was on testis transplantation, in an attempt to reverse the changes of ageing.

I

Testicular therapy was not a new idea. Indeed it was a very old one, and the most recent revival of it had started thirty years earlier in France in 1889. Charles Edouard Brown-Séquard, an important French physiologist working at the Collège de France and then at the end of a distinguished career, told a startled audience at the Société de Biologie in Paris in that year that he had succeeded in using an injection of testis extract to revive his failing powers. The seventy-two-year-old scientist, who had been plagued with multiple problems of ageing and decline, described his experiences as follows: 'The physiological effects of the extract will appear to you, as they appeared to me, most surprising. It is sufficient to state that everything I had not been able to do or had done badly for several years on account of my advanced age I am today able to perform most admirably.'

In scientific publications Brown-Séquard later described how his impotence had gone, and how he had regained better control of his bladder. But the scientific community was for the most part hostile to his claims. The respected *Wiener Medizinische Wochenschrift* complained about the content of his lecture and concluded, uncharitably, that it 'must be regarded as further proof for the necessity of retiring professors who have attained their threescore years and ten'.

The *Deutsche Medizinische Wochenschrift* was even blunter: 'his fantastic experiments must be regarded almost as senile aberrations.' The testis does produce a hormone, testosterone, but it is unlikely that this was present in Brown-Séquard's extract or played a part.

One of the reasons for these critical comments was that this testis therapy was such an old idea. The search for methods of rejuvenation to meet the desire for renewed youth has been recorded throughout medical history, and the use of extracts of testicle for sexual revival has a long and distinguished history of usage in medical therapy. Longevity has always been thought attainable: the Greek legends of a Golden Race of men who were never troubled by disease or senility were matched by other, widespread stories of 'Fountains of Youth' from many lands. Many countries boasted legends of long-lived persons, but these claims diminished rapidly in developed countries in the late nineteenth century with the accurate registration of births and deaths. The modern, sceptical era might be said to have started when, after the Bavarian census of 1871, the thirty-seven persons claiming to be over 100 years old were investigated. Only one had proof of having reached such an age, and the majority were found to be under ninety, while one man was only sixty-one years old. In Britain, as late as 1933 half the claims made by alleged centenarians were found to be untrue once the documents had been discovered and inspected.

Recipes for longevity in ancient times often involved eating the flesh of long-lived animals, and it was believed that even the blood of such an animal could have the same effect. In the Greek legend, Medea rejuvenated Aeson, the father of Jason, by means of a brew made from, among other things, long-lived deer and crows. Blood from young boys was given to Pope Innocent VIII in the last year of his life. Various theories of ageing have been proposed throughout history and continue to be produced. In the early twentieth century perhaps the best-known was that of the distinguished Russian scientist Elie Metchnikoff, who turned from investigation of the defences of the body to study ageing. He believed that old age was not a natural phenomenon. Noting that a symptom of age is the loss of special cells of the body and the over-growth instead of the connective tissue, Metchnikoff considered that the connective tissues were overactive. The cause of this abnormal tissue, he said, was the invasion of the body by microbes, coming from the large intestine. He claimed to have found an antidote to these bacteria after visiting some remote settlements where various old men with faulty memories but a liking for yogurt convinced him that yogurt held the secret of youth.

From earliest times, the testis was linked with sexual vigour, longevity and bravery: the castration of man and animals obviously had a weakening defect. Greeks and Romans used the 'satyricon' preparations made from the male testis – usually from a goat or wolf – as an aphrodisiac and a stimulant. These were sold under the name 'aquae amatrices'.

The debauches of Caligula and Nero involved these stimulants: Messalina, the notorious wife of Emperor Claudius, used such preparations to encourage her lovers. European reformers, like the distinguished physician Paracelsus, approved of sex gland extract therapy in the treatment of 'imbecility of the instruments of generation'. These extracts could not have worked. Paracelsus also claimed to have distilled from mercury a potion giving immortality. Other claims for immortality involved extracts from gold. In 1635, public interest in the testis as the controller of ageing was aroused once more when William Harvey, one of the King's physicians, carried out a post-mortem examination on the body of Thomas Parr, who had died in London at the alleged age of 152. His sexual powers had apparently continued unabated to a very late age, and the post-mortem was carried out largely because of interest in this. Harvey reported? 'The organs of generation were healthy . . . the testes, too, were sound and large.' Like other similar claimants, Parr was certainly an impostor, but the story of his vigour and healthy glands has been credulously repeated ever since. Some years later, the official pharmacopoeia of the London College of Physicians of 1676 gave directions for extraction of the reproductive organs of various species as treatment for numerous illnesses and as sexual stimulants. Salmon's *Dispensatory* of 1684 gave a similar list of animal testis extracts and their uses:

Aper, the boar . . . the stones and pizzle dried, and given in powder 1 ounce at a time, help weakness and barrenness. Canis, the dog . . . the testicles and secretion provoke lust. Cervus, the deer ... dried and drank in wine provoke lust. Equus, the horse ... excite venery and expel the afterbirth. Panthera, Leopardus, panther or leopard ... the testicle being drunk by a woman provokes the terms. Taxus, the badger ... eaten with honey, stirs up lust and causes conception. Aquila, the eagle ... the testicles cause venery. Buteo, the buzzard, the testicles help the weakness of generation. Gallus, the cock ... the testicles stir up lust. Sturio, the sturgeon ... their spawn increases seed and provokes lust.

By 1800, such extracts had disappeared from the official pharmaco-poeias in Europe, though belief in the testicle as the controller of age remained as potent as ever. Testis extracts and other rejuvenating potions were part of the wares of the eighteenth-century quacks. The great mountebank Cagliostro, who was born in 1743, toured Europe boasting of his successful use of such potions among the great and the famous.

A perceptive quack called Dr Saundby sold an elixir in Paris in the eighteenth century which was mainly pure water. The rejuvenating power claimed for it probably resulted from Saundby's rule that since the elixir was so powerful, no alcohol could be taken while the patient was under treatment. This strict regimen was the real reason for any benefits resulting from his and later rejuvenators' methods.

Testis extracts remained popular in less developed countries, and sell well to this day, though the gland is now known to have control only of secondary sexual characteristics, not of ageing. In countries with drug therapies and pharmacies not based on the orthodoxy of the Western Hemisphere, testicular extracts, usually from rare wild animals like deer, continue to be popular. Furtive use of such preparations probably continues even in the advanced countries. The majority of the world's population probably still considers that the testis controls sexual vigour and ageing.

II

So when Charles Edward Brown-Séquard claimed that a potent extract could be obtained from animal testes, many must have felt that the clock was being put back. But others reacted differently. Brown-Séquard was a distinguished scientist, and the successor to the great Claude Bernard at the Collège de France. He had made a number of innovations of major importance in his long career, including being the first to suggest that the adrenal gland produced a substance which reached and influenced the body via the blood – the first discovery of the system of endocrine glands. Thus some members of Brown-Séquard's audience may well have thought that his talents for discovery, plus his new extraction methods, had at last made it possible to obtain an active therapeutic material from the testis, which ancient methods had only imperfectly achieved. Moreover, Brown-Séquard's view was that this substance from the testis was contained normally in the seminal fluid containing the sperm. His view that this seminal fluid had invigorating properties harmonised with a popular Victorian notion that loss of semen through sexual emission – or, worse still, through masturbation – was weakening to the male.

The public rhetoric of the self-appointed experts against masturbation makes dismal reading now, but it influenced the attitudes of generations. The American public educator Orson Fowler claimed in the 1870s that 'It not only poisons your body, destroys your rosy cheeks, breaks down your nerves, impairs your digestion . . . it corrupts your morals, creates thoughts and feelings the vilest and worst possible, and endangers your very soul's salvation.' 'Wasting one's seed' in solitary pleasure, the educators claimed, led to disease, decay and even death. That mental disease could result from masturbation had apparently been put beyond reasonable doubt by a report in 1858 by Samuel Gridley Howe, and the increasing prestige and power of the medical profession in the late nineteenth century, and their increasing role as arbiters of morals as well as of health, led to uncritical acceptance of these pseudo-medical views. Expected to be miracle men, the medical profession could pontificate on many matters, and picked on this common habit as being responsible for diseases they could not cure, so cruelly shifting responsibility to the patient. Brown-Séquard's claims for a tonic from the testis not only reflected beliefs in the power of the testis which had been held from the dawn of civilisation: they also found a ready acceptance given the sexual assumptions of the day.

Two years later, Brown-Séquard and his assistant, Arsène d' Arsonval, proposed a clinical approach to endocrine disease, namely that testicular and other gland extracts be used empirically and even randomly in treating various human diseases: if success was achieved, it could be assumed that the disease was the result of a deficiency of that hormone. Called 'organotherapy', this simplistic approach was unfortunately widely followed in the next thirty years: it produced muddle and naive claims, as well as rich rewards to pharmaceutical firms and fashionable medical men, whose income from 'organotherapy' numbed their critical faculties.

Though scientific reactions to Brown-Séquard had been cool, private opinion was more optimistic and several practitioners in London obtained supplies, notably Dr Fanton-Cameron and Brudenell Carter. Some testicular extract was also sent to Victor Horsley. Better known later for his pioneering surgery of the brain and his neurophysiological experiments, Horsley had an interest in the thyroid gland; he advocated grafting of sheep thyroid tissue into patients with a possible deficiency of the gland. But it was Horsley's colleague George Murray who, using the Brown-Séquard approach, announced in 1891 the famous and correct observation that injection of extracts of thyroid gland would cure thyroid deficiency: this was the first of many successful thyroid pills.

This success with thyroid extract now made Brown-Séquard's original claim more plausible and respectable. He published a two-part article in the *British Medical Journal* in June 1893, describing the effects of extracts of kidney, pancreas, liver, sex glands, blood and blood vessels. Some of these extracts were swallowed: others were injected. The *British Medical Journal* gave a cautious welcome to this new therapy:

It is now some years since Brown-Séquard announced the wonderful effects which followed the subcutaneous injection of testicular extracts as exemplified in his own person; and though many jeered at him as the discoverer of perpetual youth, the notion has steadily gained ground that there is, after all, something in it. Since also, the success that has followed the injection of thyroid extract in myxoedema, we can hardly wonder that this belief has increased.

Shortly afterwards, a second highly potent new animal extract was announced – adrenaline – obtained from the supra-renal glands above the kidneys. The details of the discovery were typical of a time when career posts in science hardly existed. George Oliver, a Harrogate physician, was experimenting with gland extracts, usually testing them by giving them by mouth to his son. He tried new ways of making adrenal gland extracts, one of which showed some effect on the heart. On a visit to London, he suggested to his old friend Sharpey-Schäfer, the physiologist, that the extract should be tested experimentally. Sharpey-Schäfer was sceptical, but was then astonished to see the marked effects of the extract on the activity of the heart and blood vessels of animals.

The prospect of rejuvenation using extracts of testis was to entrance some medical men and scientists for the next thirty years; in the end the idea was abandoned, though the methods of extraction of other glands led to major and genuine medical advances, which must be credited to Brown-Séquard's general approach.

Thus the early days of the new science of glandular secretions – endocrinology – was a curious mixture of the respectable and the controversial. Success with thyroid extracts was undoubted, but continuing attempts to get a successful testis extract were unconvincing. Rather poignantly, the study of the organ for which an endocrine function had first been claimed had produced little. A successful testis extract had not been made, and by the 1910s the use of existing extracts was declining.

However, the failure of testis extracts to restore and revive left another possibility open to the researchers. Many still considered, rightly as it happened, that the testis was an endocrine gland making an internal secretion. Many also considered, wrongly, that it held the secret of youth. The alternative to attempting to replace testicular deficiency therefore was to transplant grafts of the gland. For other glands, transplants had been considered as equivalent to extract therapy; thyroid slices had been tried, but these were abandoned quickly, because the new extract proved more convenient and simple to use.

It was only to be expected, therefore, that testis slice transplants might be resorted to when the extracts of testis had failed. But any hopes that testis-grafting might be quietly evaluated were soon dashed. Instead, like testis extract therapy before it, gland-grafting was to be the subject of public debate and controversy in the 1920s, and the international discussion was greater, more prolonged, and more lasting than that surrounding Brown-Séquard's original announcement of his testicular tonic.

III
GLAND-GRAFTING
BEGINS

Voronoff began his new work into testis transplantation and ageing at the Collège de France after 1917 by attempting some animal experiments. He used large animals in this study, since they display the signs of ageing more prominently than small ones, and he was particularly drawn to sheep as suitable for his work. He toured the countryside round Paris collecting old rams – usually animals which were 'kept for affection rather than breeding'. Many others came from the Arles region, in the South of France. Once he had built up this stock of old animals in his laboratory, he began his experiments, grafting the older animals with testis gland slices from young rams, and placing the slices beside the older animals' own testicles.

These experiments were reported in scientific papers to learned societies and later published in orthodox medical journals. One of the animals treated is shown in Fig. 4 and is described as showing the beneficial results of a testis graft. The lady shown holding the grafted animal is probably his laboratory assistant, Evelyn Bostwick, the rich, twice-divorced American whom he was later to marry. Voronoff's claims for these experiments were spectacular, particularly for the effects of testicular slice grafts on young castrated rams and aged rams. Castrated rams normally have no interest in sexual activity, are of a low weight, and have small, thin horns. In the castrated animals grafted by Voronoff he claimed that sexual activity returned to normal, as did weight and horn growth. His results with the old rams were, he said, similarly successful. Voronoff showed photographs of Old Ram No.12 which had, he said, arrived at the laboratory in a pitiable state of old age, looking unwell and suffering from trembling and incontinence. Two months after a testis transplant, he reported that the animal was completely transformed. Gone were the tremors and incontinence, and some months later the old ram fathered a fine vigorous lamb.

Voronoff's claims cannot be believed, since his testis grafts would have rejected in about one week. There were some major defects in his experiments which led to these false claims. The necessary desiderata of such an experiment are firstly, that there should be a 'control' group of animals: all the animals should have been split at random into a group which received the operation, and one which did not. Voronoff failed to set aside such a group of non-operated 'controls'. Secondly the outcome of the procedure should have been measured in some way, by weight and height, or activity, or breeding performance. Although in the early twentieth century this approach was not yet firmly accepted in biological science, Voronoff ignored even the basic rules of such experimentation. No measurements were made, and only some of the operated animals were described in his articles. Doubtless the 'best' results were chosen for the report, and only the best of the best were photographed. Worse still, the animals which did not show the expected improvement were dismissed as failed grafts.

We must take his word for it that some of the rams did indeed show apparent revitalisation, but in the absence of the precautions mentioned above, other explanations for the 'rejuvenation' present themselves. The animals may have been diseased when obtained from the farms, and their health may have improved in the laboratory; or they may have been underfed before being moved to his animal house. Lastly, it should be noted that Evelyn Bostwick, his assistant, was an ambitious person without laboratory training, and as such she might well have been over-anxious to produce the desired scientific result: such helpful assistants have been blamed for errors in other laboratories. It is now known, for instance, that Alexis Carrel's famous claim to have succeeded in keeping some heart cells alive outside the body tissue culture was probably a fraud: his assistants are thought to have regularly introduced fresh cells into the cultures to 'keep the boss happy'. Even Mendel's monks may have been anxious to produce the desired result for his plant-breeding experiments, since their figures are suspiciously close to the theoretical prediction; while Pavlov, confronted with a serious error, reported that an assistant had produced the suspect data.

However, there was other evidence produced by Voronoff to suggest that the transplanted glands were working. He had operated again on Old Ram No. 12 one year after its graft, and removed the grafted tissue for microscopic study. This investigation was carried out by Édouard Retterer of the École de Médecine, Paris, later Professeur Agrégé in the Faculté de Médecine. Retterer was to be a supporter of Voronoff in the years to come, and his firm conclusion that the grafts had not been 'absorbed', i.e. rejected, was crucial support for Voronoff's work. After studying the tissue in this way, Retterer reported that parts of the transplanted graft were still surviving.

Voronoff was perhaps unlucky to have this continuing support from his eminent colleague. The cellular changes in rejection are not easy to unravel and understand, and Retterer mistook the invading cells seen in the graft as persistence of the graft itself: instead the cells he saw were those which had rejected the graft. Voronoff was no microscopist. He had to take Retterer's welcome reports on trust, and these descriptions were wrong. Perhaps Retterer's judgement was in turn swayed by Voronoff's charismatic confidence.

For his goat testis transplantation, Voronoff used only the transplanting of slices of the organ. As in skin grafting, the ingrowth of new blood vessels would quickly nourish the grafts, and it was hoped that at least some cells would survive and grow. It was usual in grafting slices of tissue to put them into muscle, but Voronoff rejected this conventional approach. Accordingly, he used an alternative *méthode* which, he was to insist, was essential for success. He grafted the testis slices onto the roughened surface of the recipient's own testis, where they were held by stitches: he insisted that the blood supply to the normal testis had a unique quality of possessing stimulating substances, so it was necessary that the graft was placed on the surface of the patient's own testis. Like many of Voronoff's ideas, there was an immediate plausibility about this idea, but there was no scientific basis for it. His *méthode* is described in detail later.

I

In October 1919, Voronoff gave a scientific paper on his gland graft work to the annual meeting of the Congrès Français de Chirurgie – the French Surgical Congress. The French press briefly noted his contribution, perhaps being notified of it by Voronoff. The story was taken up in London, and on 8 October 1919, the *Chronicle* gave an account of the paper Voronoff had given to this Paris congress. It described his experiments on rams and goats, and his claims to have restored ageing animals to full vigour by use of the 'interstitial' gland – a term modestly used by Voronoff instead of 'testis'. Moreover, Voronoff was quoted as saying that 'there is no reason not to do so on man.' The story was repeated in the world's newspapers, including the *New York Times*. Some of these added that Voronoff had worked at the Rockefeller Institute, but an unidentified spokesman at the Rockefeller Institute, possibly Carrel, when asked to comment, said that such gland grafts were unlikely to succeed.

In spite of this, there was world-wide public interest in Voronoff, who was almost alone in his pursuit of tissue transplantation research. The pre-war interest in transplantation among conventional scientists had not revived after the end of the First World War. One reason for this was obvious. On the continent of Europe, medical science was at a low ebb. The greatness of the German medical schools had gone, and there was starvation in Vienna; German medical scientists were ostracised by the international community because of their call for war in 1914 and the German use of poison gas in the war. French research institutes were impoverished, and in Britain the new Medical Research Council, firmly led by its single-minded secretary, the physiologist Walter Fletcher, supported the basic medical sciences rather than applied clinical research. Surgical research hardly existed in continental Europe, and even surgeons in Britain interested in research were to get little or no support from official funds.

These findings suggest a gulf between clinical practice and laboratory studies in the 1920s and 1930s. This was particularly true in Europe, where full-time hospital academic posts hardly existed, and medical men like Voronoff had to support themselves with a career in private practice. Not surprisingly, clinical research in Europe was reserved for dilettante, fitting it in as a spare-time hobby in between treating private patients. European surgeons appeared to have little contact with basic scientists, and clinical science failed to progress on a continent in the aftermath of war.

Nor was transplantation immunology a favoured basic science. In Britain, the Medical Research Council did not favour immunology. Before the First World War, one man E. F. Bashford, had almost reached what would now be considered a sensible view on tissue transplantation. Working as the scientist in charge of the new Imperial Cancer Research Fund laboratories, he was near to concluding that grafts of cancers on normal tissue were regularly rejected, but the war interrupted his work, and he died in 1914. After the war, the I.C.R.F. moved over to studying the tissue culture of cancer cells. In the 1920s the new American medical scientists, though productive and self-confident, were less cosmopolitan and were poor linguists; they tended to ignore the older European literature, especially when émigrés like Carrel had little good to say of his old teachers back in France. But some Americans, like Voronoff's admirer Thorek, were still dazzled by the great traditions of European clinical science. To them, Voronoff was a *savant* who had inherited the mantle of authority from his predecessors in Paris, including Pasteur and Claude Bernard.

But perhaps the main reason for the eclipse of tissue transplantation in the early 1920s was that Carrel himself had moved on to another topic of research. Although he had been awarded his Nobel Prize for transplantation in 1912, from 1910 he had concerned himself instead with devising methods of growing cells outside the human body. In this he was largely successful – and, as usual, involved in controversy over his failure to acknowledge the help and work of others.

The effect of this curious hiatus in transplantation development in the 1920s and 1930s – which was to continue until 1948 – was that Voronoff was largely left alone with his claims, unfettered by more careful and orthodox colleagues.

II

Instead, one of the first groups to comment on Voronoff's remarkable claims in October 1919 to have rejuvenated the old rams was the anti-vivisectionist lobby in Britain. Dr Walter R. Hadwen, the formidable editor of the anti-vivisection journal, the *Abolitionist*, who was to thunder from its columns against Voronoff for the next twenty years, made some quite sensible remarks on graft rejection in the course of his first broadside against the Paris surgeon:

We doubt if the old ram ever left the condition of senility at any stage. The French (or Russian) professor probably mistook the excitement of fever, due to the decomposition and absorption of the constituents of the transplanted gland, for the liveliness of rejuvenation . . . One of the Rockefeller vivisectors has, however, warned people not to be led away by Dr Voronoff's confident claims . . . an amusing instance of the invariable rule that you can always trust on vivisector to contradict the conclusions of another . . . the world will discover yet again that modern science and quackery are twin sisters . . .

Next week there were more newspaper reports of Voronoff's work, stating that he had been deluged with inquiries about the possibility of gland transplants in human patients. However, a footnote was added to one of these stories in *The New York Times* during that week: 'In reference to the reports from France that Dr Serge Voronoff's researches were based on a series of experiments at the Rockefeller Institute in 1910, the Institute state that Dr Voronoff was unknown to its officers and staff and has never worked there in any capacity.'

Clearly the Rockefeller Institute was being careful to dissociate itself from Voronoff. Alexis Carrel had now returned there from France, and doubtless he was consulted about this press release. Possibly he wanted to distance himself from Voronoff's claims; if, as has been suggested, he had supported Voronoff during the war, it could be that he was now worried that such claims might discredit him. If so, Carrel showed shrewd judgement, and subsequent events entirely vindicated him.

Ten days after the conference, Voronoff was in the news again. On 18 October 1919, he announced that human glands would remain healthy in the body for three hours after death, a claim which was almost correct. Hence, if a young healthy man was killed in an accident, Voronoff proposed that the body should be rushed to special hospitals where the glands could be removed, then 'grouped' (i.e. blood grouped), and stored for later use. On the same day came news from America of just such an approach to gland-grafting. In San Quentin Prison in California, a convicted murderer, Thomas Bellon, had been executed. His testicles were immediately removed and transplanted into a prematurely aged sixty-year-old inmate of the prison. The operation had been carried out by Dr Leo L. Stanley, then aged thirty-three, the medical officer in charge of the prison medical department. He was later to perform over thirty such operations, and many more implants of testicular fragments on the prison inmates. Prisoners were used in this way in American medical research until the 1970s, usually for monetary reward or hope of parole, and many other prisons, notably the Indiana State Penitentiary, were to try rejuvenation experiments. Stanley's cases were later reported in the reputable journal *Endocrinology*, and were claimed to be successful: later, he and the San Quentin authorities forgot they ever had an interest in the whole business. But in the 1920s the San Quentin prison administration were proud of Stanley's achievement, and, for some years after, press releases described this work, including the creditable performance of the transplanted patients at the annual prison sports.

It is important to note that, at this point, Voronoff had not carried out a human testicle transplant. His scientific papers and the publicity which had surrounded them in October 1919 had only involved animal experiments: Dr Stanley's work at San Quentin had preceded Voronoff's, though Stanley himself was not the first to do a testis graft. As a result of the publicity, there was soon to be a lively controversy about who should get the credit for the first such human gland grafts. Voronoff was to be rather late in entering the human testis transplant field, and as a result of his success in identifying himself with the operation, he was soon to be criticised for claiming priority. Much later, however, the other pioneers and their biographers were happy to let Voronoff take the credit for the operation.

III

The intensity of interest in rejuvenation at this time is striking and contrasts with the lack of interest in transplantation in general. It may simply have been one of the periodic bouts of interest in attempted rejuvenation to which mankind is prone, but the fact that the monkey gland enthusiasm appeared just after the First World War and was centred on Europe suggests that social factors were at work which made the public receptive to the idea – the most obvious of which was that Europe had lost a huge number of young men in the First World War. The young officer group had suffered particularly heavy losses. The well-off families of Europe had lost their sons, and older men grudged their age more acutely than usual. Not only that, but from 1880, the birth rate had been going down in Europe, families had become smaller, and by the 1920s, governments were urging their people to increase the size of their families. The War was blamed for Britain and France's slower rate of population growth, and in both countries patriotic fears were raised of a loss of Empire through depopulation of the Mother Country. E. J. Smith of Bradford, a man of affairs, and author of *A Yorkshireman Abroad*, wrote in his book *Race Regeneration* (1918):

If the higher civilisation we claim is to continue to influence the world, we cannot allow our numbers to fall more rapidly than those of nations and empires which stand for meaner conceptions and grosser forms of life. Such numbers cannot be maintained, however, unless drastic measures are immediately taken to avert this national calamity.

Great Britain has unconsciously become an old and dying community; old, because owing to the declining birth-rate of the last forty years there are now three middle-aged persons for every two young children; and dying, because apart from the war, the progressively growing disproportion means that notwithstanding increasing longevity and the fall in infantile mortality the deaths of old people must ultimately exceed the births of infants. To this well-defined trend, we have now to add the rapidly extending employment of women in new fields of service which, though a necessary emergency measure, is likely to become more or less permanent and, with the terrible loss at the Front of those who would otherwise have been our best fathers, is bound to increase still further the ominous fall.

In this post-war world of concern for the ageing male and population decline in the USSR and Europe, it is hardly surprising that the gland-grafters had a not unsympathetic hearing. A leader–writer in the *Military Surgeon* poignantly hoped that such methods would go away: 'For us who . . . steer a more or less successful course for a definite term of years between the Scylla of matrimony and the Charybdis of frailty, it seems as though in the time of our setting sun we ought to be absolved of the necessity of following again the primrose path which is for the feet of young men to tread.'

This interest in the fertility of the upper classes was shared by the eugenics movement. This had been started by Francis Galton (1822–1911), who pointed out that the human race might influence its own evolution. Galton claimed that talents, and in particular intellectual gifts, were inherited; he played down the role of environment, and proposed that, by judicious marriage, in consecutive generations a highly gifted progeny would arise. Galton's views had little practical impact, but after the appointment of Karl Pearson to a post teaching eugenics in the University of London in 1906, the thrust of the eugenic arguments moved from positive proposals for the intellectual elite, to studying those who might be dragging down the human race – alleged to be the lower classes, criminals and the mentally ill. The concern for 'national degeneration', together with the war losses and evidence that there was a higher birth rate in the lower classes than the middle and upper, created a receptive audience for the new 'negative eugenics', which wrongly supposed that intelligence as well as many illnesses were hereditary, and proposed limits on working-class fertility and the prevention of breeding by the mentally subnormal, epileptics, the mentally ill and criminals. Legislation followed in many countries. In Britain – where the cause of the Empire and reversing 'national degeneration' were invoked – legislation was initially confined to constraints on the mentally handicapped. In the USA the misleading statistical data produced by the eugenicists resulted in more stringent legislation, and by 1931 compulsory sterilisation laws were in existence in twenty-seven states to deal with the 'unfit'. In such an atmosphere, hostility in the USA to particular racial groups and to immigrants was given a pseudo-scientific backing. In Germany the excesses of the Third Reich in its persecution and elimination of non-Aryan people, selective breeding experiments and killing of the insane, were the results of extreme interpretations of eugenic doctrine.

Voronoff was not closely involved in the eugenics movement of the early twentieth century. He was not claimed as one of their number, nor were his views discussed widely within the movement. But his work and attitudes carry the stamp of some of the assumptions of the times, including those of the eugenicists. If the First World War had destroyed a fit elite and had left a degenerating, elderly rump, Voronoff's own efforts at rejuvenating the ageing wealthy class was at least a step in the right direction. The possible physical and sexual revival of wealthy men who were past their prime was in harmony with the spirit of the times.

Taken together, many of the hopes and assumptions of the 1920s and even 1930s amounted to claims and plans to alter the human constitution and hence influence the human race, in both its numbers and its vitality. Just as in the USSR Lamarkism was popular and harmonised with Soviet expectations that successive generations would prove better socialists, so the eugenics movement hoped to encourage breeding by the élite and discourage others. The new endocrinologists among medical men explained much in the human character in terms of the body's glandular state and balance, and suggested that therapy could influence this balance. In schools and the army, elaborate physical training schemes were introduced in the mistaken view that these encouraged growth and strength in the young. Even the growing skills of orthopaedic and plastic surgeons were seen as contributing to the changing of man by science. This notion that science would conquer all was reflected in the works of H. G. Wells and others. Julian Huxley predicted that 'biological knowledge would enable us to modify the processes of our bodies more in accord with our wishes.' The human body and the race, like the human condition, were seen as plastic, malleable in the hands of the scientist. Voronoff and his like were merely symptomatic of claims to be able to tinker with the human race.

IV

The San Quentin testis transplants caused widening ripples of international interest in gland grafting and in Voronoff's work. In Paris, the daily newspaper *L'Humanité* noted that the talk of the town in the autumn of 1919 was rejuvenation rather than politics. Another French newspaper, *L'Oeuvre*, raised the first of a number of ethical pseudo-problems which logically followed if gland transplants could indeed succeed in rejuvenating animals or man. Was it morally justified, the paper asked, to extend the life of a life-sentence prisoner thus making a life sentence longer, as had been done at San Quentin? Considerable debate on such spurious ethical problems took place during the gland transplant enthusiasm of the 1920s. These discussions ignored and obscured the vital question – whether or not the gland transplants worked. Indeed, they simply assumed that they did.

Early in 1920, the first celebrities to announce that they had received rejuvenation treatment made their news public. Such announcements were to become quite frequent later. Seeking such treatment often reflected a genuine need for a restoration of vitality. Those involved had often been prominent in some way, and tended to be out-of-work film stars or, more poignantly, writers whose output and invention had declined. In making public that they had received gland treatment these passé celebrities hoped to persuade others that their talents had been restored. The first such announcement was made by Frank Klaus, the American former middleweight champion of the world. Clearly he felt that rejuvenation by grafting would help him regain his crown, and he publicly announced that he was undergoing the treatment. The American surgeon and hospital involved were not named: and nothing was heard of Klaus afterwards.

V

Eight months after the first news of his method of rejuvenation by gland grafting had been made public, Serge Voronoff and his new wife arrived in New York. They had travelled on the *S.S. France* and the boat docked on 18 July 1920. His great talent for publicity ensured that he was now enough of a celebrity for his travels to be of public interest. Voronoff had remarried earlier that year at the age of fifty-three; his new wife was his laboratory assistant, Evelyn, Countess de Périgny, née Bostwick, the divorced daughter of the deceased American Standard Oil millionaire Jabez Bostwick, the partner of John D. Rockefeller. Described as short in stature, with fine chiselled features and a wealth of Titian hair, she was on her third marriage, and was neither European nor young. And, like many of the rich well-connected women wandering in Europe doing war work, she had a number of personal problems, probably involving drink and drugs, which were to shorten her life.

She had been a nurse in both the Boer War and in the First World War. She then worked in the Collège de France as Voronoff's personal assistant, and was acknowledged as such in his scientific papers. She also endowed the Collège de France's Division of Experimental Surgery, headed by Voronoff, with substantial funds from Standard Oil shares to continue its work. As a result, Voronoff had fallen on his feet: not only had he married a talented scientific assistant, who could also help him with translations into English, but Evelyn was fabulously wealthy.

Though the Bostwick family fortunes were rather tangled, in round terms Madame Voronoff was worth about $3,000,000. Jabez Bostwick had died in 1892, while attempting to rescue his horses from a fire at his Long Island Farm. Evelyn had been his favourite daughter, and she and Mrs Bostwick had been well provided-for. Evelyn stood to gain even more money in the event of her mother's death. This had occurred in July 1920, and Dr and Mme Voronoff were in America in the summer of 1920 to wind up her mother's affairs.

On disembarking from the *S.S. France*, Voronoff uncharactistically declined to speak to the press, in spite of rumours that he had recently carried out testis transplants into human patients. The reason for his reticence, as suggested below, was that he had a major problem on his mind.

Some time after their arrival in New York, the medical correspondent of the *New York Times*, Van Buren Thorne, M.D., managed to arrange an interview with the Voronoffs at the Bostwicks' substantial family house at 800 Fifth Avenue. Thorne was not a novice at medical journalism, and he had been a key figure in the earlier lionisation of Alexis Carrel by the *New York Times*. It is therefore likely that Thorne was exceptionally well briefed on the problems of transplantation before his interview with the Voronoffs. He may even have discussed the matter with Carrel.

He was received, he recounted, by Madame Voronoff. She explained that her husband's English was poor, and that she would speak for him since she was closely associated with his scientific work. Moreover, she explained somewhat disingenuously, his position as a government employee at the Collège de France meant that his scientific reports had to go first to that institution, and he preferred not to release his detailed findings until then. Early in the interview Thorne put an important question. Had Voronoff carried out a human testis transplant using monkey testicles? Madame Voronoff quickly answered this point. Dr Voronoff had not carried out any such human testis transplants in October, she said, though some newspaper reports claimed that he had. She went on to deplore the attentions and distortions of the press. Her husband was, she stressed, a serious scientist, and she complained that even in France there had been public ridicule of the idea of monkey gland transplants. Lastly, she made a claim that was to be made many times later. She was emphatic that testis transplantation was not intended for sexual rejuvenation: rather it was intended to treat the broader problem of premature ageing. She blamed the salacity of the media for distorting the true nature of their work.

Though publicly confident, The Voronoffs were concealing a serious problem. In fact, as emerged later, Voronoff had carried out monkey-to-human transplantation shortly before his departure for America in June 1920 – and both cases had gone badly wrong. The Voronoffs must have been upset, and were doubtless anxiously awaiting further news from France. The monkey gland transplant operations had been carried out on 12 and 21 June 1920, and they left for America on about 10 July. The clinical details of these cases were honestly given by Voronoff in later publications. Both patients were men whose testicles had been totally destroyed by tuberculosis.

Shortly after the operations in which, for the first time, monkey testis grafts were transplanted, there was obvious infection in both wounds and in both cases the grafts had to be removed. Patients with testicular tuberculosis were hardly favourable subjects for Voronoff's transplants, since the normal tissues and the normal landmarks had been destroyed and continuing infection might have been present. These failures must have weighed on Voronoff's mind during his visit to America. After his public pronouncements on his grand schemes for transplanting glands, it must have taken some determination to continue. No doubt he and his wife decided not only to keep silent about these two cases, but – for once – to avoid the press.

In spite of Madame Voronoff's confidence and composure, Van Buren Thorne felt it necessary to ask another awkward question at the end of the interview. What about the claim that Voronoff had spent some time at the Rockefeller Institute? Madame Voronoff was clear in her answer. In 1910, she said, Dr Voronoff had indeed done research work there for nine or ten months. Thorne was charitable enough not to pursue the matter or to press the point that this claim had previously been denied by the Rockefeller officials. And what of Carrel, asked Thorne? He is a friend of ours, Mme Voronoff replied simply. Lastly, asked Thorne, had other surgeons done human testis transplants? She agreed that this was so: Dr R. T. Morris of New York and Dr Frank Lydston of Chicago had done such surgery. The Voronoffs were less careful about acknowledging these other glandgrafters later.

VI

Understandably, Voronoff took care not to be prominent while in New York. But one month after his arrival, he agreed to demonstrate his gland-grafting technique at the College of Physicians and Surgeons in New York. The demonstration involved the use of anaesthetised dogs both as the donors and recipients of the testis transplants. In view of the public interest, the meeting was confined to members of the college. Voronoff and those members present did not make any comment afterwards, other than to confirm that the meeting had taken place. This silence had probably been enforced by the College.

This meeting, and Voronoff's presence in New York, pleased one surgeon, Max Thorek, but annoyed at least one other, Dr Frank Lydston. The reason for Lydston's pique was that he could claim to have worked on gland-grafting for a longer period than Voronoff. George Frank Lydston was a respected Chicago surgeon of sixty-two. At one time he had been Professor of Genito-Urinary Surgery and Venereal Disease in the College of Physicians and Surgeons in Chicago, and in addition to his considerable scientific writings and the publication of three textbooks and medical works for general readers, he had also written adventure books and novels. Max Thorek, his friend and surgical colleague in Chicago, described him as a persistent man who never did anything by half – 'owing to his Red Indian blood'. In 1914, six years earlier, Lydston had carried out a number of human testis transplants, reporting good results of transplanting human testicles into patients with a variety of degenerative conditions, including senile decay. These effects had been described, without public fuss, in a number of orthodox medical journals. Not only that, but Lydston even carried out the operation on himself in 1914. One year before Voronoff's visit to America, Lydston had taken Thorek aside and astonished his colleague by showing him what he said was the transplanted testicle in place close to his own testicles. Lydston told Thorek that the transplant had invigorated him greatly: but he was deceiving himself, and the 'transplant' must have been a lump of rejected tissue.

This earlier personal testimony by Lydston now encouraged Thorek to investigate further the question of testis transplantation. When Voronoff's public claim for success was made in 1919, Thorek was one of the first to write to Paris asking for further details of the French surgeon's methods and results. Voronoff had replied quickly and enclosed the required data which, to Thorek's dismay, was written in French. Thorek, impatient for information, found to his delight that one of his long-stay patients in his hospital ward was a languages teacher. With this patient's help, Thorek had the works of Voronoff translated, and commenced gland grafting in Chicago in 1919.

So when Voronoff came to stay in New York in 1920, two surgeons at least were vitally interested in his presence. Lydston was annoyed that Voronoff appeared to be taking the credit for inventing the operation, but Thorek was delighted to have his elegant French hero on American soil. A third medical man, of some notoriety, was also vitally interested, and was to make an attempt to meet Voronoff. This was 'Dr' John R. Brinkley, who regularly transplanted goat testicles to patients in his private clinic in rural Kansas, and could also, with some justification, claim to be a pioneering testis transplanter, and had certainly preceded Voronoff in carrying out the operation.

Lydston made the first move. On 15 August he wrote to the *New York Times*, making clear his claims to be the pioneer of the testis transplant operation. He reminded readers that he had operated on his own body on 16 January 1914 and on a number of patients later. These cases were subsequently described in scientific articles, where he concluded that testis transplants were beneficial. He reported that they retarded development of senility, cured grey hair, and cured the skin disease of psoriasis and reversed defective sexual development.

He also pointed out that even earlier, in 1912, two Americans called Hammond and Sutton had attempted such a testis transplant. In addition, another Chicago surgeon, Victor Lespinasse, may have done the operation even earlier, in 1911. Commenting on Lydston's letter, the *New York Times* complained that America was failing to get the credit for these discoveries and that patients were mistakenly travelling to Europe for such treatment. In fact, said the newspaper, such surgery was available in their own country. Each city in America, claimed the *New York Times*, had a surgeon who could carry out gland transplantation.

Thorek did not share Lydston's antagonism to Voronoff, and was very anxious that Voronoff should visit Chicago. The French visitor initially appeared reluctant to do so, but after Thorek had travelled to New York and been graciously entertained, Voronoff agreed to lecture in Chicago at the American Hospital. Thorek was delighted at the success of the occasion. The lecture theatre was packed with medical men and Voronoff's considerable presence, his flair for the *mot juste*, and the novelty of the necessary translation of his French lecture by an interpreter, Dr Aimé Paul Heineck, all combined to make the occasion memorable for the audience.

There was, however, one unpleasant incident: Frank Lydston refused to attend. Voronoff had sent him a gracious personal note which acknowledged Lydston's pioneering work, and in it he added the hope that Lydston might attend the lectures. Lydston declined to do so, and so appeared to be churlish. But he had, however, some justification in avoiding the occasion. Although Voronoff in private was scrupulous about acknowledging the priority and research of others, he conspicuously omitted such courtesies in public and in his publications. Three years later, in 1923, Lydston died of pneumonia, at the age of sixty-five, without having forgiven Voronoff. His obituaries record that he was active in the field of gland grafting. The *American Journal of Clinical Medicine* said his work in this field was a pioneer effort, 'he being the first one who ever undertook such an operation. His controversy with Voronoff is in the minds of us all, and we are fully aware of Lydston's priority in this particular field.'

VII

Of the other Chicago doctors in the large audience listening to Voronoff we know little. One medical man, 'Dr' Brinkley of Kansas, was determined to attend, but was kept out. His claims to be inside the auditorium listening to Voronoff were excellent: the organisers' reasons for keeping him out were also entirely reasonable. 'Dr' Brinkley had been gland-grafting in rural Kansas since 1917, but it was far from clear that he was medically qualified at all, and his publicity-seeking caused continuous irritation.

Although Brinkley's claims to hold three M.D. degrees were all extremely dubious, he was to be a millionaire by 1930 as a result of his celebrated goat gland transplantation operation. His own accounts of his medical education were confirmed neither by later legal investigators nor by his biographer, Gerald Carson. Brinkley attained his qualifications at a time when higher education was patchy in quality. It was later established that his arts degree from the National University of Arts and Science at St Louis was fraudulently obtained from a corrupt official: in 1915 the registrar of this 'diploma mill' was bribed to back-date the degree to 1913. In

May 1915 he managed to persuade one of the many run-down medical schools in USA – the Eclectic Medical University of Kansas – to grant him a diploma. American medical education at that time was an odd mixture. The well-known conventional medical schools were excellent, but there were also small basic medical schools which a pluralist and individualist society still permitted to survive. Brinkley's diploma required only three months of study. The little medical school's normal course lasted one year, but Brinkley claimed that his earlier degree allowed him credit. Few states recognised the Eclectic Medical University of Kansas, but Arkansas was one of them. Having obtained an Arkansas licence, Brinkley later managed, through reciprocity agreements, to obtain a Kansas licence as well. It should not be thought that Brinkley was necessarily ignorant. On the contrary, in his later appearances before courts and tribunals he clearly showed much conventional knowledge and skill in medical prescribing. He also defended his surgical technique with convincing anatomical knowledge, though eye-witnesses said his operating technique was poor.

After wandering about the southern United States, including some brushes with authority and some unpleasantness over unpaid bills and bouncing cheques, Brinkley settled in Milford, Kansas, a tiny town of 200 souls to the west of the capital, Topeka. It was an unlikely place in which to contemplate setting up a successful private medical practice: but perhaps the small mid-West town gave him a sense of freedom.

In October 1917, two weeks after his arrival in Milford, he did his first gland graft. This was carried out four years before Voronoff's first case. He was no doubt inspired by the first published reports from Lydston and others in Chicago: but while Lydston had used human donor glands, and Voronoff was to choose the monkey as the donor animal, Brinkley turned to the goat as his donor of testicles. In choosing the goat, he ignored major immunological barriers to success. But to the simple country people of the mid-west the goat was a symbol of sexual prowess and stamina. Brinkley had another justification for using this animal, and one which may have saved him from problems with his grafts: the goat had a reputation for good health and was not susceptible to tuberculosis. The same cannot be said for monkeys, whose many diseases could be transferred with the graft.

Brinkley's first patient to be grafted had originally consulted him for infertility. Following Brinkley's goat gland transplant, the patient later fathered a boy, who was then named 'Billy' to mark the occasion. The local newspaper ran the story of the transplant: more patients appeared to request the operation from Brinkley.

Brinkley tells the story of this pioneer operation with almost credible detail in his ghosted autobiography, *The Life of a Man*:

A very peculiar circumstance happened at Milford, Kansas. I had only been there about two weeks, being a new doctor in town and having a little drug store that I had opened up there, and different country people would drop into the drug store to meet the new doctor and pay me their respects and tell me they were glad I was there and so forth. This one man came in and got to talking with me about sexual weakness. I told him I didn't know anything that would do him any particular good as to sexual weakness. The conversation continued and we got to talking about why couldn't we take some glands out of an animal and put them into a man. I told him it was biologically impossible. He wanted to know why it was impossible. I told him because you couldn't transplant the glands from a higher order of animal kingdom to a lower or vice versa. He wanted to know how I knew you couldn't, and I told him that was what I had been taught and I believed it. To make a long story short, he furnished the animal and I transplanted some glands into him, with good results according to his statements to me. I had advised the man not to have it done and he said, 'You are a surgeon. You can put them in and if they spoil you can take them out'. To me the results were amazing and startling because I expected bad results and disastrous results and instead of that happy results were obtained. The man claimed that he had been sexually dead for sixteen years. His wife verified that statement. A year later I delivered his wife of a fine baby boy, which at least proved that he was fertile anyhow. Of course the news got around in great fashion, and a cousin of his came to me and asked me to do the same thing on him and I did and he had me to transplant glands into his wife. Then one of their relatives was in the insane hospital in Nebraska. He had been a banker. He was a banker up there, he was a cashier and lost his mind and was placed in an insane institution. They wanted to know from me if I thought glands would do this insane person any good, and I said, 'Lord God no', and they said, 'We want you to try it' because he had been a masturbator and 'We know it' and they brought him down there, took him out of the institution, and I put those glands into him and that man recovered his mind and today is in charge of one of the biggest banks in

Kansas City, Missouri. He came out of the insane asylum in Nebraska and had those glands put in. I published that in an article in a little magazine, and down in Alabama a lady read it. She had a daughter that had been in the insane asylum for ten years in Tuscaloosa, Alabama. She was violently insane at times. When she went to get a permit, she had to get a state permit to get this daughter out of a padded cell, they had to keep her in what is called a padded cell to keep her from doing injury to herself; she was trying all the time to commit suicide. And my wife and I met this lady with her daughter in Memphis, Tennessee, and put her in the drawing room and brought her to Kansas City and over to Milford. I transplanted glands into that young lady. She stayed in my hospital for a month, fully recovered her mental capacity. She didn't want to go home because she felt she was disgraced because of her previous life. She secured a secretarial position in Kansas City, Missouri, and married a physician and today she is healthy and happy and normal.

By summer 1918 Brinkley had built his own hospital in the tiny town of Milford and the goat gland work was beginning to exceed his ordinary medical practice. He now used the Toggenberg strain of goat, because of their lack of odour. These he bought from a part-time postman, preacher and goat dealer in Arkansas, who later described Brinkley as a good customer and one who promptly paid his bills. The goats were kept in a pen near the hospital. After removing the required glands, the carcasses were, as Brinkley said, 'fed to the coyotes'.

But Brinkley soon came to the notice of American medical men when he moved from Milford and tried to settle in Chicago and continue gland grafting there. His suspect medical degrees and his aggressive publicity methods made it easy for the medical establishment in Chicago to deny him a licence to practise and hence have him moved out of town back to Milford. Brinkley blamed Thorek for this, and he was probably correct. So it was hardly surprising that when Brinkley attempted to attend Voronoff's Chicago lecture in 1920 he was prevented from doing so.

But these reverses were of little consequence to Brinkley, and his goat gland transplants became known to a wider audience as the result of a slim book published in 1921. This was an account of Brinkley by Sydney B. Flower entitled *The Goat Gland Transplant*. The writer himself had undergone the operation and had suffered no ill effects. One reviewer remarked of this pamphlet that it contained a dearth of facts about the operation, but considerable detail on how to reach Dr Brinkley's hospital. It was at about this time that Dr Brinkley introduced into his promotional literature the useful phrase 'You are only as old as your glands'. This appealing concept was to be fixed in the public consciousness for many decades, since the 1920s were a time of public preoccupation with the glands of the body and their alleged links with a wide range of disease and debility.

VIII

In the autumn of 1920 Voronoff returned from America to Europe with his wife. But America was to hear of him again later that year when he published a book on the general theme of gland transplantation.

His book was called *Life*, and the English version was translated from the French by his wife. It was well reviewed, and may have sold well. Its publication was important to Voronoff. He had been late into this field, and had done only a small number of experimental grafts, but to publish a book on gland grafts, and a well-written one, placed him at the forefront of public and even professional attention. It was a remarkable coup. In the book he used an argument which was to recur in his writings. Carrel's work had shown, he said, that cells grown outside the body are immortal. Therefore old age is due to poisons or a deficiency. The obvious deficiency is the atrophy of the testis, *ergo* testis grafting will cure old age. Voronoff mounted a plausible array of evidence for this thesis. He begins by saying that castration is associated with premature ageing and loss of vitality, not only in gelded horses but also in human eunuchs and in patients with loss of both testicles. Voronoff used classical allusions, quoting the story according to which the poet Abelard never wrote again after his castration. He also credulously cited the cases of Goethe, whose long life he credited to well-preserved genitals, and Thomas Parr, mentioned earlier. In explaining his use of the monkey as a donor, he said that this choice was initially forced on him by the lack of human donor glands. However, he found that not only did the monkey glands succeed, but they survived better than human glands, because of their 'virility'. The monkey (a chimpanzee in his early work, and baboon later) was chosen simply because it was so close to man, and Voronoff pointed out that this species shared many of the blood groups of man.

As a result of the book, his name was to be linked forever with gland transplantation, especially as he had made no mention of earlier attempts, including those of Lydston. This failure to acknowledge other workers was noticed by a reviewer – van Buren Thorne, who had interviewed the Voronoffs in the previous year. Thorne's review in the *New York Times* was almost entirely taken up with showing that gland grafting was an American invention and that it had been routine in major cities for some years.

Not all medical men were swept along in this wave of enthusiasm. The *Journal of the American Medical Association* was cautious. In an editorial of 16 October 1920 it said: 'At present, there seems to be a sort of international scrambling for priority recognition in the alleged discovery of the profound secret of restoring lost youth and youthful vigour ... One must marvel at the ease with which fragmentary data are woven into a story of technical success.' But the journal did not think such transplants did not work. The thrust of the editorial was to call for more information. One cautionary note was struck: current opinion was that a transplanted gland would only work if the patient's own similar glands were absent. This doctrine had the authority of William S. Halsted, Professor of Surgery at Johns Hopkins. Halsted's Law, as it quickly became known, was never confirmed, and was a mistaken conclusion made by this distinguished surgeon.

On his return to Paris, Voronoff had the melancholy job of re-operating on his first two human testis transplant cases and removing the infected, dead monkey grafts. But by the end of the year he had done four more gland transplants. As before, he failed to obtain a supply of human glands. Though he turned to monkey donors instead, he hinted that pressure had been put on him by potential patients to find human donor glands. He made it known that human donors prepared to give one gland for transplantation would be welcome. Two men volunteered, but their fee was too high, so he continued to use grafts from the monkey.

Little is known of the source of his early donor monkeys, but they may have been bought from travelling circuses or from the laboratories of the Pasteur Institute in Paris. He used chimpanzees early on, but all the animals used later were baboons. In the early operations he was assisted by Drs Didry, Baudet or Dartigues, whose skills he frequently praised. The operations were carried out at private clinics in Paris, usually the Maison de Santé in the Rue Montaigne, the Maison de Santé Ambroise Paré at Neuilly or at the Villa Molière.

The four cases carried out in late 1920 were much more successful. His patients are described in later publications as 'a civil servant' aged fifty-nine, a French 'man of letters' aged sixty-four, an American 'man of letters' aged thirty-three, and a Spanish engineer aged sixty-six. In none of these patients was there any pre-existing active local disease in the testis area. The patients' complaints were of premature senility or general debility: sexual decline or impotence was also complained of in all cases. These operations went well, with the exception of infection and necrosis in one graft, on one side on one patient, but the patient's remaining graft on the other side survived. Voronoff must have been delighted that there were no major technical complications. Moreover, all patients, he claimed, showed improved intellectual and physical powers, and three of the four reported increased sexual activity. One of them returned three years later for a second graft, when he felt the benefit of the first had worn off. So 1920 ended well for Voronoff. The secret, embarrassing failures with his first two cases were now behind him, and his American visit and his book had been successful.

Next year – 1921 – was not a busy one for Voronoff, and he performed only two human testis transplants. However, one of these cases was a particular success and was of considerable importance, since the patient was to stand by Voronoff and defend him in his time of crisis.

IX

1921 was marked by growing enthusiasm in America for rejuvenation by grafting. Much of the activity centred round Chicago, doubtless as a result of the presence there of Lydston and Thorek.

Thorek later wrote that 'in the 1920s, fashionable dinner parties and cracker barrel confabs, as well as sedate gatherings of the elite were alive with the whisper – "monkey glands". Rejuvenation had been discovered ... Voronoff, reputable scientist in the Collège de France, said so.'

Gland transplantations of all kinds were taking place. In late 1920, the Chicago American Hospital, where Lydston and Thorek worked, announced that a mentally defective nineteen-year-old girl, Mary Zembock of Joliet, Illinois, had had a successful monkey thyroid gland transplant. In February 1921 a Chicago chef, Otto Trobach, issued a plea to be considered for a testis transplant operation. Both his testicles had been destroyed in a car accident, and he appealed to the prison authorities in Cook County to provide the glands of the next criminal to be executed in their institution. Another news story told of a thirty-nine-year-old physically frail American, George Hauser, who received a gland graft from an executed criminal in 1920. An author, Irvin R. Bacon, had a similar transplant carried out in the Majestic Hotel, New York, the cost of which was paid by the *New York American* newspaper. This operation was carried out by Dr Thomas W. Edgar. Bacon had expected a fee of $4,000 from the newspaper for his story, but was paid less, and shortly before the story appeared, the journalist disappeared. His distraught wife attributed this to financial disappointment or some sinister side-effect of the new operation. Some time later the truth came out: he had simply decided to leave his wife and live with another woman.

Another journalist visited John R. Brinkley in Kansas and had the goat gland operation. He was delighted with the result and described it thus: 'The author had the operation himself suffering no ill effects and ten days later could work long hours day after day with no sense of mental fatigue but a certain gaiety of heart accompanying successive days, as if life were rather a lark, he being accurately introspective and not easily deceived into optimistic conclusions.' This was all self-deception.

As well as these testicle transplantation stories, there was also a good deal of enthusiasm for thyroid gland extract treatment for conditions much broader and less well-defined than simple thyroid deficiency. On 19 October 1921, Dr Frank G. Bruner, Director of

Special Schools, which provided education for the mentally sub-normal in Chicago, announced that he was impressed with the work done on the transplantation of monkey and goat glands for reviving physical functions. He went on to say that a sheep thyroid gland diet would be used thereafter in the special schools to feed the sub-normal children. 'We expect to meet with success . . .' he said.

X

Voronoff was not the only European rejuvenator. Eugen Steinach, an Austrian working in Vienna, entered into the field when he reported that remarkable rejuvenation could be obtained in elderly rats by gland transplantation. He performed similar experiments to Voronoff's, using guinea pigs instead. While Voronoff can be charit-ably excused in his erroneous experiments with elderly rams, Steinach's mistaken conclusions from conventional laboratory ex-periments invite censure. Indeed Steinach claimed that an ovary graft under the skin of old guinea pigs resulted in the revival of their ovaries and subsequent pregnancies. This claim is so erroneous that allegations of fraud in these and other experiments must be made, and similar charges have been made about his colleagues' work as well.

The work of Steinach and his group must be seen against the background of post-war Viennese medicine. Steinach's ex-perimental animal work had been carried out before World War One, when Vienna was still the centre of the medical research world. But at that time Viennese biology and medicine, like Austrian culture, showed a spectacular mixture of brilliance and decadence. In the Biological Institute – the 'Vivarium' – where Steinach was head of the section on Experimental Biology, this mixture was particularly marked. Paul Weiss, who made substantial contribu-tions to biology, worked there; but so too did two men – Paul Kammerer and Theodore Koppanyi – whose work later became suspect and controversial.

After World War One, Austria was demoralised and destitute. Rampant inflation had ruined the economy, and private wealth had been destroyed. No support of scientific research by public or private funds was possible. Of the original Viennese biologists at the

Vivarium, Weiss and Koppanyi had left for America. Weiss is now famed for his experiments on regeneration of the optic nerve. Koppanyi, in not dissimilar experiments carried out in Vienna, claimed to be able to transplant whole eyes between unrelated rats – experiments which could not have succeeded. He either deceived himself or deliberately misled others. Though he enjoyed a brief fame, and his experiments were described in *Scientific American*, his claims have been decently ignored. After leaving Vienna and briefly taking up an appointment at a small American college, his career after 1924 cannot be traced. His colleague Kammerer's allegedly fraudulent experiments are described later. An aura of unreliability surrounds the scientific work of the Vienna Vivarium, which included Steinach's and Koppanyi's unlikely grafts, and the tampering with Kammerer's midwife toads.

But in post-war Vienna, Steinach prospered. He found that rejuvenation therapy was good business, and, for reasons which are not clear, he offered not gland transplants but his own rejuvenation operations. Of these, the best known was his operation for males, widely known as the Steinach operation. This, he claimed, had worked in experimental animals. The operation was a simple one and is now used for male sterilisation – namely vasectomy, or the cutting the vas deferens, the tube carrying sperm from the testis. There is no rejuvenating effect from this common operation. Steinach called it 'vasoligation' and performed it in some cases only on one testicle. In this way, fertility was maintained.

The theory behind Steinach's rejuvenation operation was seldom fully explained. He claimed that since the operation prevented sperm from leaving the testis, it had an invigorating effect. This met a favourable public acceptance, since it harmonised with the murky Victorian sexual myth, discussed earlier, that masturbation was harmful: if loss of sperm and seminal fluid was weakening, ergo abstinence or surgical blockage of the loss must be strengthening. By the 1920s, responsible medical opinion had dropped this stance, but it left the plausible theorem that since masturbation is weakening *ergo* abstinence or surgical vasoligation was stimulating.

For female rejuvenation, Steinach offered radiation of the ovaries. The hazards of ionising radiation were not then appreciated, and

Steinach was one of many who used irradiation in this ineffective and apparently irresponsible way.

Steinach's fame spread, as did Voronoff's; the world was ready to accept his claims. There is more than a hint that the post-war Austrian government were backing Steinach as a symbol of hope for the resurgence of Austrian medical research back to its former authority. All the continental nations of Europe, notably Germany and France, had been demoralised and impoverished by the Great War: the possibility of a scientific success story and a medical break-through therefore appealed to politicians. In November 1920, the Austrian State Government announced that they were helping to make a scientific film about rejuvenation, which described in detail the Steinach method. Dr Hainisch, President of the Republic, had taken a personal interest in this project, it was said, and the film was widely distributed later. The Austrian government propaganda department put out a press release, stating that the film had been acclaimed in Austria and Germany. Their description of wild scenes of enthusiasm among those who queued to see the film, which had 'before and after' shots of rejuvenated rats, can hardly be taken seriously. Later the film reached America. Not surprisingly, an American financier and some physicians proposed a company with $1,000,000 capital to establish an Institute for 'Juvenescence' in Vienna, the home of the Steinach operation. It is not known whether this project was ever established or succeeded.

In America Steinach had an impressive supporter in a popular New York physician, Harry Benjamin, who took an enthusiastic interest in the problem of old age and decline. He and his 'Life Extension Institute' investigated many therapies, and Benjamin was the most vocal advocate of the Steinach operation, though Steinach had to ask him to make less strident claims.

Until now no concern had been expressed about the possible side-effects of the rejuvenation operations. But on 12 May 1921, the death in London was announced of Alfred Wilson, a wealthy septuagenarian, who had made his money in ship-breaking. This otherwise unremarkable event arroused interest because some months previously he had gone to Vienna and had undergone the Steinach operation. On his return to London he had felt so well that he booked the Albert Hall in London to deliver a lecture entitled 'How I Was Made Twenty Years Younger'. A little while before the lecture he had visited his doctor and complained of some chest pain. Both doctor and patient agreed that this discomfort was the result of Wilson's new habit of hitting himself on the chest to demonstrate his renewed virility. However, the pain probably came from a coronary artery disease and Wilson dropped dead from a heart attack twelve hours before giving his lecture. At the inquest into the death it was mentioned that Dr Steinach had charged £700 for the operation.

In the 1920s Steinach also undertook respectable research. Using the money from the fees from his rejuvenation practice, he built up a research group which then gained support from the Schering Aktien-Gesellschaft, who were interested in identifying and manufacturing the hormones of the sex glands.

XI

Though Steinach and Voronoff publicly vied with each other in lectures and press comment, Voronoff's place at the head of the rejuvenation movement was now established. But the year from mid-1921 to mid-1922 was crucial to him. He had been late into the gland-grafting field, but as a result of his book he was now an established figure in international medicine. That same year a major change took place in his life. He had always been well off; now he became immensely rich. Evelyn, his wife and former assistant, died in 1921 after one year of marriage. The cause of death is not known, but she drank heavily and may also have had a problem with drugs.

His wife's death made Voronoff immensely wealthy, but the complexities of his inheritance were considerable. The first, and smallest, component involved the estate of his late father-in-law, Jabez Bostwick. In Bostwick's will a capital sum had been put in trust for his daughter, with the income to go to her during her life. On her death, the interest was to go to her husband; on his death the capital was to go to their children. But Voronoff had problems with the capital sum which should have passed to him and any such family, since Bostwick had stipulated that if Madame Voronoff's husband and children were not resident in America or were not citizens of America, they were not to receive anything, and the money was to go instead to Wake Forest College, North Carolina. Neither Voronoff himself, nor his wife's children by her previous marriage were American. During 1921, Voronoff and his wife's children contested this stipulation, but lost their action in the American courts. The capital sum, amounting to about $800,000, was given to the college; but the stipulations in the will about the interest from this capital sum were less clear, and Voronoff must have been delighted when the courts awarded him the income during his lifetime. His was to be a long life, and the sum awarded was roughly $80,000 per annum – which in the 1920s would have ensured him a comfortable independent existence, to say the least.

But this substantial income was small in comparison to what he was to gain from his wife's own estate. Not only had she been receiving the income from the trust established by her father, the income which was awarded to Voronoff, but when her mother died in 1920, she was the preferred beneficiary in her will. Three-quarters of the considerable estate which had been left to Mrs Bostwick by her late husband Jabez now passed to Madame Voronoff, and the rest to a second daughter. Madame Voronoff's own fortune at her death was finally valued at $3,750,000. But she had not left the entire sum to her husband: he had to be content with the income only, and on his death the capital was to be divided among her children of previous marriages. From 1922 onwards Voronoff was to receive an annual income from this source of $245,000, in addition to the $80,000 income from the Bostwick trust.

Voronoff was now immensely wealthy and had the security of a huge dependable income. This financial security must have helped to stiffen his resolve to survive in the year of crisis which followed. It also meant that Voronoff had no financial motive for his persistent advocacy and use of gland-grafting. He need never have worked again: he simply wished to be famous.

XII

There was, at this time, little outright condemnation of the gland graft operation by medical men or others. Since biologists showed little interest in transplantation and the available data in the scientific literature was confused, the few scientific studies of transplantation were poorly planned and executed. Worse still, many shoddy articles were still appearing in medical journals claiming success with skin grafts between humans. These persisted until the 1940s, when such grafts were abandoned and skin was taken thereafter only from the injured persons themselves. In the period after the First World War it was seldom claimed that *all* skin grafts could take, but that *some* human skin grafts could take permanently when grafted from one person to another. Such claims seemed plausible enough. Serious scientists described how skin grafts would survive if the newly-described blood groups were matched in the donor and recipient. Others described how skin from new-born animals or babies did not reject. A steady supply of foreskins from circumcised human beings found its way to be put ineffectively on other humans' burns or ulcers. The gland-grafters could take encouragement from this apparent success with skin and also from the increasing and genuine success of special cases like cornea-grafting (i.e. replacing the transparent front part of the eye) and the use of bone-grafting. Moderate medical opinion was not opposed to the claims for monkey gland transplants. Moreover, moderate opinion could also agree that gland grafting methods were in their infancy, and could be improved.

But there were some authorities prepared to speak out on important occasions, and in 1920 Dr Arthur Dean Bevan, President of the American Medical Association, took time in his Presidential Address to attack gland grafting: 'It is a scientific fact that any foreign gland introduced into the human body must disappear within a short time. This is as elementary and incontrovertible as that two and two are four.' But he may not have been talking of human-to-human transplants, or even Voronoff's monkey-to-human grafts, because Bevan then went on to attack 'transplant quackery'. It may be that, as an official of the American Medical Association, he had Brinkley, not Voronoff, in mind, and he may even have approved of the work of Voronoff and Stanley.

Thus there were few who believed strongly that the gland transplants could not succeed. But there were some critics of monkey gland-grafting who raised moral and ethical objections to such transplants. They either deplored the reported effects of the transplant or the use of animals as donors. These critics assumed that Voronoff's transplants worked and in doing so they must have aided his success. Such ethical pseudo-problems produced a rather hilarious gloss on a shaky science.

But at this point in 1921 it is remarkable how little scientific data were available to enable anyone to form a mature judgement on testis transplantation. Certainly, Lydston of Chicago had recorded four such cases, but Stanley, of the San Quentin Prison gland transplants, did not publish his series until 1922, and even then it was brief and anecdotal. The goat gland transplanter, Brinkley, was not the type of man to record and publish data, and never gave an account of his work or even of his surgical method. Lastly, and more importantly, Voronoff, the man widely believed to be 'the gland graft specialist', had not made public his results with human patients. Public interest was based on little information: no doubt people wanted such transplants to work.

In 1922 studies of gland transplantation at last found their way into the literature. First Stanley, and then Voronoff and others, published their results.

Dr Stanley's experience of gland-grafting at San Quentin prison appeared in the journal *Endocrinology*, where he reported impressive results in 643 inmates who had been given grafts or testicular extracts for a surprising range of problems. In addition, it was reported that thirteen physicians had received this type of treatment from Dr Stanley. According to Stanley, his ageing recipients were rejuvenated, and gland-grafting also improved acne and asthma. Stanley's report seemed particularly credible, since his work did not suffer the same disadvantages as that of other gland transplanters, namely that follow-up of their patients was usually poor and was accompanied by changes in diet and habits. Instead, Stanley's follow-up of his incarcerated patients was inevitably good. The prison environment was unchanging; in particular, the grafted patients had no change of food. While Voronoff wisely encouraged rest and temperance for his weary, rich, private patients, which helped the alleged rejuvenation effect, such abstinence has always been the lot of the lifer. But there was unspoken pressure on the prisoners to produce the expected result: parole or payments could be the reward of such experiments.

On 19 June 1922, Voronoff issued a statement fully reported in the *New York Times*. He was, he said, now doing human monkey gland transplants regularly, using the testis for the correction of the defects of old age, and he added, in a vivid phrase, that he could now 'put back human ageing by twenty to thirty years'. He let it be known that he was paying most of the costs of the operation himself, including a $500 bill for each chimpanzee. He hinted that there was now a long waiting list for his operation.

At the end of this press release Voronoff hit out at his critics: 'It is stupid that many American and English surgeons insist that my method is a failure. I have not made a report to any Society since I began my operations. I will give a complete report in October.' It was a bold statement. Certainly he had not made any reports, and he had done only about ten grafts. Voronoff saw himself as a scientist. He felt that his few cases were more important than Stanley's longer series. However, this apparent desire for anonymity was hypocritical. Though he frequently made disapproving comments about the attention of newsmen, and claimed that a distorted view of his work was being presented, there seems no doubt that he sought their attentions and steadily provided copy for them.

The meeting to which Voronoff referred was the annual meeting of the French surgeons – the Congrès Français de Chirurgie – to which society he had spoken previously on his goat transplant work. It was to meet four months later, on 5 October 1922. One of many organised by the rather conservative Académie de Médécine, it was to provide the first of two major crises in Voronoff's professional life: on this occasion he was to survive and rout his critics.

IV
CRISIS AND SURVIVAL

The day before the meeting of the French Surgical Congress on 4 October 1922, a small item about gland-grafting appeared in the Paris edition of an American newspaper, the *Chicago Tribune*, simply stating that Voronoff would make a sensational announcement at the meeting next day. Whether or not Voronoff himself had issued this press release is not clear – it could be that an attentive journalist had constructed the story from an advance copy of the printed proceedings of the conference next day – but it seems likely that Voronoff had inspired the story personally. His paper had already been printed, and Voronoff had sent a copy on ahead to the *British Medical Journal*, with a translation into English. He had made careful plans to give his news to the world, and he may well have encouraged the attentions of the *Chicago Tribune*.

At the meeting next morning, held in the Sorbonne, there was no hint of the scandal to come. Voronoff was scheduled to speak at a session chaired by Professor Henri Hartmann, a senior academic in the Faculté de Médecine, and a clinician who had made considerable contributions to surgery of the bowel: one of these standard surgical operations still bears his name. But instead of calling on Voronoff to speak, Hartmann rose and told the audience that although Voronoff was scheduled to address them, his paper had been withdrawn by the organisers of the meeting.

The reason for this serious action was, Hartmann said, that Voronoff had broken the rules of the Congress – one which is commonly found in the rules of other societies, whereby research work given in scientific papers to the Congress should not have been published previously. This sensible rule encourages the presentation of new work in progress and discourages doctors and scientists from appearing at research meetings simply to repeat old research work which they have already described in print. Voronoff's mention in the press the previous day was the cause of Hartmann's ruling, but it could hardly be called a publication within the scope of this prohibition, though doubtless it annoyed the Congress organisers. For Hartmann to have prevented Voronoff from speaking as a result of this technical violation of the rules suggests a deep hostility to Voronoff by the French Surgical Congress in general, or by Hartmann in person. The audience's response made clear their hostility to Voronoff. When he came to the platform and attempted to justify himself, he found it impossible to speak through the barrage of noise from the assembled members. Other accounts of this incident, which was reported in the world press next day, say that Voronoff denied responsibility for the newspaper reports, but that Hartmann waved a paper and shouted 'Here is proof.' Others say that Voronoff shouted 'coward' at Hartmann. But in the end, Voronoff was prevented from speaking, and he left the hall. This noisy and unpleasant scene, probably without parallel in the history of any scientific society, lasted for ten minutes. There was, however, a tradition at the Academy of noisy and emotional debate. Declamatory criticism was common, and some years earlier Pasteur had defended his germ theory of disease at Academy meetings of this type.

After leaving the meeting, Voronoff acted quickly to give his side of the story to curious newspaper reporters. The ostensible cause of the incident – the newspaper account of his work – was, he claimed, not authorised by him, so he was innocent of the breach of the Congress rules. He admitted that the opposition to him went beyond this mere technicality: there was, he said, an organised conspiracy against him, drummed up by jealous colleagues. The controversy continued next day. In a short statement, Professor Hartmann confirmed the ruling that published research could not be presented to the Congress and he explained unconvincingly that newspaper publication was included in this rule. He added, rather unkindly, that there had even been some initial opposition by the organisers of the meeting to accepting a paper to be given by Voronoff.

I

There appears to be some justification in Voronoff's allegations of a vendetta against him. Firstly, there is little evidence that gland grafting was scientifically controversial at that time. Lydston and Stanley in America had already claimed success with the operation. Nor was Voronoff or his work unknown to the Congress, since he was well-known in Paris and had spoken to the society about his animal gland work two years previously. In 1919 he and his collaborators had also given two papers on the same topic to the Society of Biology. Moreover, Voronoff had an orthodox research post in an eminent establishment in Paris: he was within the scientific establishment. It is difficult not to conclude that opposition to Voronoff was the result of personal hostility towards him, doubtless resulting from his love of publicity and his use of the newspapers to describe his work. There was no French medical ethical code forbidding such personal advertising, but probably there may well have been strong unwritten rules against it, and Voronoff had given the Congress an opportunity to rebuke him. Moreover, a successful private practitioner like Voronoff would have had enemies.

Next day Voronoff began a skilful defence of his reputation. In a new statement, he portrayed the French Surgical Congress and the Academy of Medicine as decaying, rundown organisations who opposed all change and innovation. Many people agreed with this view. Voronoff pointed out that the Academy of Medicine had a poor record in accepting new ideas, and on one famous occasion had been badly wrong. In 1882, some members of the Academy of Medicine had openly opposed a paper given by Louis Pasteur and continued to oppose him. Indeed, he recalled that when he was a student in Paris, the students had been warned not to quote Pasteur's 'germ theory' of disease in front of these unsympathetic teachers. One man, Professor Peter, had been prominent in the opposition to Pasteur's germ theory. In defending himself, Voronoff skilfully suggested that Professor Hartmann had now taken on the conservative mantle of the discredited Professor Peter.

World interest in this French surgical scandal increased when one of Voronoff's patients joined the controversy – a seventy-six year-old London businessman, Edward Liardet, who, the *New York Times* said, looked forty-five years old. Liardet had received a monkey gland transplant on 2 February 1921, twenty months before the conference, and had been delighted by the result, which, among the other benefits of rejuvenation, included the loss of his *embonpoint*. He had been given a new life by his operation, he told reporters, and he was amazed at the hostile reception given to Voronoff by the Academy. Moreover, he added, Voronoff had never charged him a penny for his operation: instead Voronoff had personally paid the heavy costs of the monkey gland transplant.

That same day, Voronoff also announced that he would soon defend himself in public. The scientific institution in which he worked – the Collège de France – would allow him to lecture on his work and demonstrate his animal experiments. A date was fixed for the 8th of October. Voronoff's plan was reminiscent of Pasteur's famous public defence of his work by a display of the success of anthrax vaccination in flocks of sheep at the farm of Pouilly-le-Fort. Not for the first time, Voronoff took comfort and inspiration from the example of Pasteur.

II

On 8 October, Voronoff gave his postponed lecture. His usual eloquence was enhanced by a demonstration of nimble grafted animals and the personal testimony by his patient, Edward Liardet. There was a good turn-out of medical staff from his own institution, but medical men from the rest of Paris were, according to the newspapers, conspicuously absent. The only doctors to attend from outside the Collège de France were Dr Retterer, who had been closely associated with Voronoff's work, and a Dr Manoeuvrier of the University of Paris. The absence of medical people does not necessarily imply criticism of the scientific content of the lecture: they may simply and understandably have wished to avoid the likely publicity.

But Voronoff's gamble paid off – as had Pasteur's. Next day, Paris newspapers came out solidly on his side. Some of the French papers echoed Voronoff's anti-establishment theme and the editorials complained of the conservative attitudes of the 'official scientists' and of the 'dead wood of age and honours'. But Voronoff not only won the public battle: he seems to have won his professional struggle as well. In the next few months and years, his scientific papers on gland transplantation and others by his colleagues were accepted for presentation at French medical and scientific societies, and given a proper hearing.

Later that year, Voronoff published an eighty-five-page monograph describing his gland-grafting. Entitled *Greffes Testiculaires*, it had been prepared for distribution at the French Surgical Congress, but could not be circulated because of the controversy: the slim volume – which is now a collector's item – has a title page which erroneously describes the paper as having been given at that meeting. This monograph was the first of Voronoff's works to be noticed by the medical press, and is described in a review in the *British Medical Journal* of 21 October 1922. The review noted that the paper had not been given to the Congress 'since some objection was taken'. It makes little comment on Voronoff's methods and theory, but gives a lengthy summary of the monograph, and uses long quotations from it without comment.

By this time it is clear that in France and elsewhere it was being conceded that Voronoff was, perhaps, onto something. Indeed, a few months later the same conservative Academy of Medicine listened in respectful silence to a paper given by another French surgeon, Dr Francis Heckel, on monkey gland transplants. Heckel started his talk by saying he had been curious, though sceptical, about Voronoff's methods, and had accordingly studied them at first hand, watching Voronoff at work. Heckel went out of his way to say that Voronoff had been helpful 'in the gracious way known to us all'. He had seen seven patients treated by Voronoff, including one of Heckel's own, and these operations had been successes. He presented this patient to the meeting, and made out a convincing case for his rejuvenation. Dr Heckel added that patients were applying in hundreds for the operation. Most of them, he said, were men of between fifty and sixty years of age who, he added poignantly, had 'some life's work to finish or some vital enterprise which had not been crowned with success'.

Shortly afterwards, on 3 February 1923, the Society of Biology accepted a paper on the 'Structure of the Chimpanzee Testicle and Physiological Effects of its Transplantation' by Professor Retterer and Voronoff. It was presented and later published. Voronoff's reasons for using monkey glands were set out with his usual style. He wrote:

I used the glands of monkeys in this and subsequent *greffes testiculaires* on men because the securing of human glands presents serious obstacles, and because the glands of monkeys, and especially those of the anthropoid apes, are the only ones that can furnish grafts which will find among human tissues the same conditions of life that they had originally. To use the glands of other animals is to ignore completely the laws of biology: they could never be, in the human organism, anything but foreign bodies. The anthropoid apes form a race very close to the human race. Their embryology, their dentition, the analogy of the skeleton, the skull and the internal organs, furnish abundant proof of the biological parentage of man and monkey. The blood shows the logical parentage of man and monkey. The blood of the chimpanzee differs less from that of man than it does from that of other species of monkeys.

Reading this elegant statement, it is not hard to understand why the plausible gland-grafter had such a following. Voronoff assumes that the reader agrees that human-to-human transplants can work. Then he alleges that recent work had shown that some monkeys, particularly the chimpanzees, are more closely related to man than to monkeys; hence their tissues can be used as grafts. Voronoff's plausibility is enhanced still further when he denounces the use of other animals, since this would ignore the 'laws of biology'. Even today, the reader of Voronoff's apologia has to be reminded that his monkey grafts into the human body were totally destroyed in a few days.

III

By the summer of 1923, only six months after his humiliation by the Congress, Voronoff had succeeded in getting guarded approval for his work from medical men in France – an acceptance which continued and increased in the year to come.

At the highly orthodox and respected International Surgical Society meeting in 1923, a speaker from America, Dr Charles A.

Frazier, said of Voronoff's methods that 'his success in isolated cases is not disputed, but the benefit was always likely to be temporary.' This view was not unreasonable: moreover, it was shared by Voronoff, a fact which had important consequences for his practice and his income from the operation. Voronoff agreed that some grafts might fail, and he was prepared to do a second transplant on the same patient. His view was that the first transplant might be 'absorbed' in time, necessitating a repeat operation. First grafts from monkeys to human beings are destroyed quickly through their rapid rejection by invading cells and serum: a second graft into a person who has rejected a first graft is destroyed within minutes.

Steinach had also wisely decided that a second operation was necessary for those who thought that the effects of his first operation had worn off. Since he could not repeat the ligation operation, he removed the narrow fluid-filled cavity which surrounded the testicle. This, he said, made new vessels grow into the testicle which 're-energised' the gland.

In 1923, Voronoff had a busy, scholarly summer. He attended and spoke at the Sixth International Congress of Surgery held in London in July 1923. Sir William Macewen was president and the Prince of Wales welcomed the guests, together with the Minister of Health, Mr Neville Chamberlain. Professor Hartmann was presented to the Prince as a representative of the French surgeons attending, but British newspapers seemed more interested in Voronoff's presence. Neville Chamberlain's introductory remarks to the conference must have pleased the monkey gland-grafter:

The State is like a hive of bees – the drones must never be allowed to outnumber the workers. Anyone who by reason of bodily infirmity is not able to make his full contribution to the service of the community is a drone, a parasite, a burden instead of a source of wealth and strength. Surgery is daily converting drones into workers, and thereby placing the community in its debt.

Voronoff gave his paper on monkey testis grafting to the London Conference, stressing that six doctors had been among his patients. In the audience of surgeons, Voronoff had an admirer: Ivor Back, a well-known consultant at St George's Hospital, London, spoke in the discussion after Voronoff's lecture and supported his work. Back

– who eventually became President of the British Medical Defence Union – was one of a number of British surgeons who took an active interest in Voronoff's work. To a conventional career of some distinction he added temporary enthusiasms for novelties; he was now in his early forties and had a number of orthodox publications to his credit. His interest at this time in testis transplantation may have led him to carry out the operation in London. This doubtless embarrassed him later, and his obituaries do not mention it.

Immediately after the London conference, Voronoff's collaborator, Professor Retterer, travelled north and reported on their work to the International Congress of Physiology at Edinburgh, giving a paper entitled 'The Relations between the Physiological Phenomena and the Structure of the Grafted Testicle'. Voronoff's collaboration with the pathologist Retterer continued for some time. It was a vital partnership for Voronoff, who had no experience with the microscopic study of tissue. Retterer repeatedly assured Voronoff that when he examined specimens from Voronoff's experiments, the grafts were still living even years after grafting. In fact Retterer was wrong: the living cells he saw and described were instead cells of the host which had grown into and destroyed the graft.

On 29 July came encouraging but tragic news for Voronoff. In Buenos Aires a gland graft had been attempted on one of the country's most famous race horses, Yrigoyen. At the age of ten, the horse had broken down physically, and had failed to breed. In an attempt to restore vigour the gland graft was resorted to. The horse died three hours after the operation as an effect of the anaesthetic.

IV

In the autumn of 1923, the next meeting of the annual Congress of French Surgeons at Paris came round again, one year after Voronoff had been humiliated. There was a set-back for Voronoff in the run-up to the meeting: Edward Liardet, his star patient, who had defended him one year before, died a month before the conference was due to begin. Surprisingly, this did not damage Voronoff's rising reputation. Liardet's personal medical history was well known, both from his testimony for Voronoff one year previously, and also from the rather embarrassing details of his case given in Voronoff's publications, which show that Liardet had suffered from gonorrhoea several times, and was a chronic alcoholic. Voronoff made it clear that Liardet's death took place during an attack of delirium tremens – and the testis graft, he suggested, could not have been expected to cure such intemperance.

Voronoff had resigned from the Congress because of their treatment of him the previous year, and although he was present, he did not speak at the meeting. However two senior and respected French surgeons presented scientific papers on gland grafting work they had carried out as assistants to Dr Voronoff. These men – Dr Dartigues and Dr Baudet – described forty-four monkey testis transplants to human patients, all with allegedly good results. Included among them were some performed by Ivor Back of St George's Hospital in London.

An even more interesting speaker at the Congress was the Chicago surgeon, Max Thorek. Thorek was an early admirer of Voronoff; he had enthusiastically hosted the Voronoffs during their visit to America three years earlier, and had arranged for Voronoff's successful lecture and demonstration in Chicago. Since then he had been using Voronoff's gland transplant methods on patients in Chicago. It seems likely that Thorek had an official invitation from the officials of the Surgical Congress – which suggests that official interest in testis transplantation in France was growing and provides further evidence that Voronoff's reputation and his methods had been restored to respectability. Thorek described this visit as one of the high points of his career, and he records that his address to the Congress was enthusiastically received by the audience of distinguished French *savants*. He was proud that Voronoff was in the audience, and he was delighted when the French surgeon praised his results.

Thorek then travelled on to Rome, where he spoke again on gland grafting to the International Conference on Comparative Pathology. He was, he recounts, once again an invited guest, and this was reflected in the generous allocation of time given by the organisers for his lecture. Warming to his theme, Thorek spoke for two hours, reviewing his experience of ninety-seven testis transplants; his paper was later published in full in the respectable scientific journal, *Endocrinology*.

Apologies for absence from this lecture and from the Rome meeting were given by Signor Mussolini and Serge Voronoff. Voronoff had planned to travel to Rome, but may have been detained in Paris through pressure of work. He had a number of testis transplants to do, not all of which were on human patients. Four surgeons who had attended the earlier Congress of French surgeons had requested monkey gland transplants for themselves, and these were carried out that week; and one week after the Paris conference, he carried out a pioneering operation – his first gland-graft on a horse. The operation was carried out at the Veterinary School at Alfort, France's most prestigious veterinary training centre, and its director, Professor Petit, was enthusiastic afterwards about Voronoff's method. Petit's interest continued for many years and he and his veterinary colleagues were to defend and stand by Voronoff to the last. The grafted animal was a former champion race-horse and its virility, and hence its earnings as a breeder at stud, had declined. Although the operation had been sponsored by the newspaper *Liberté*, the result was never made public. This first venture into work with livestock was an important step for Voronoff: for his animal experiments were to cause the second crisis in his professional life. Race-horses are less liable to suggestion than human beings; confidentiality does not apply to veterinary work, and breeding figures speak for themselves.

Although he had missed the Rome conference because of these surgical operations, Voronoff was in high spirits when Thorek returned from Rome to Paris. Thorek was again hospitably treated by Voronoff, and in his memoirs he recalls an astonishing parting scene between the two eminent gland-grafters. A few minutes before Thorek's train departed from the Gare St Lazare, Voronoff thrust a surprise gift upon his guest. It was a monkey – a chimpanzee named Roger. For once, the confident American urologist's *bonhomie* was ruffled, especially when, as an experienced clinician, he noted that the chimpanzee had been de-glanded. Having made the supreme sacrifice for one of Voronoff's patients, Roger was useless, even for experimental work. Roger caused considerable trouble during the train and boat journey back to America, and the emasculated chimp spent the rest of his peaceful and embarrassingly long life in Lincoln Park Zoo, Chicago.

Thorek continued his gland-grafting work in Chicago during the 1920s, and eventually published a book called *The Human Testis*. To carry out this work, he built a monkey house and laboratory on the roof of the American Hospital in Chicago. One Sunday morning the monkeys escaped and, descending into the town, made for the Catholic church of Our Lady of the Lake. In his memoirs Thorek said that he could not describe in print the 'sacrilegious actions of these monkeys'. Voronoff had similar troubles from time to time when these inventive and resourceful animals escaped. On one such occasion two rich Neapolitans wished to have the operation, and Voronoff arranged that he would travel to Naples and carry out the operation there. The patients had agreed to buy their own monkeys first, and this they did. However, the monkeys escaped and lived for a short time in the Naples Royal Park. From there they were chased into a church where they climbed up the bell ropes, ringing the bells wildly before being eventually recaptured.

V

The few years that followed were the peak of Voronoff's career. To add to his huge inherited income he had an increasing income from his gland operations, for which he now routinely charged between £500 and £1000, an astonishing sum, though he often announced 'free' operations in press statements. By now he had settled into an agreeable routine: since he was personally paying for his research unit, he could arrange his own timetable. He spent the summer months from May to October in Paris, staying at the same suite on the first floor of Claridges on the Champs Élysées. His valet, chauffeur and secretary occupied smaller rooms in the servants' quarters on the top floor. In Paris it was well-known that he had two mistresses. His prestigious attachment to the Collège de France was still a sham, and it seems that he never carried out any further research or teaching there. Instead, his time was spent carrying out his one operation on private patients and travelling. In the winter he did no surgery but moved to the Riviera: patients wanting a transplant had to wait until the spring. Like Hippocrates, Voronoff felt there was a season appropriate to each treatment.

Voronoff's surgical methods can now be described. It must not be imagined that the testis transplants of the 1920s bore any similarity to the kidney or heart transplants of today. In modern transplants, the blood vessels of the organ are carefully sutured to the patient's own arteries and veins. Testis transplantation, on the other hand, was more akin to skin grafting: the graft, or slices of it, was simply placed in the body, and new blood vessels grew in within a few days and nourished the graft. If the graft was a thick one, only the outer layers survived.

It hardly mattered where the graft was implanted, nor how it was done, but Voronoff always insisted that the details of his technique were essential to its success. His technique is described in detail in his *Greffes Testiculaires* of 1924 – translated into English as *Rejuvenation by Grafting* – and in Dartigues' text. In addition, we have an eye-witness account of his technique by the Edinburgh veterinary surgeon, William C. Miller, whose account is given in Appendix I to the Report to the Ministry of Agriculture on Voronoff's method. Voronoff did not favour the usual plan when grafting thin slices of tissue of putting his slice grafts into the rectus muscle on the front of the abdomen. Instead, he transplanted his grafts onto the surface of the patient's own testicles.

In an adjacent operating theatre, the donor monkeys were anaes-thetised and their testes displayed. An illustration from Dartigues' book shows that each gland was sliced into six pieces, and that each monkey gave enough grafts for two patients. Meanwhile, the patient was prepared, using local anaesthetic, and the surface of the testes exposed. This is easily done, since the testis is surrounded with a fluid-filled cavity – the *tunica vaginalis*.

Voronoff grafted three donor testis slices to each testis in each patient, stitching them in position after deliberately scarifying the testis surface to encourage new blood vessel growth. The tunica was then closed over the area of the grafts. Though he probably chose this scrotal position for the grafts to impress the patients, Voronoff used an interesting argument to rationalise his choice. He felt that the fluid in the tunica nourished the grafted slices until new vessels had grown into the grafts. This notion was directly derived from Alexis Carrel's discovery of tissue culture methods which would keep cells alive. The idea that the testis graft could be nourished in this way is superficially attractive, but any survival of the graft in fact depended on the usual ingrowth of vessels from the surface of the patient's own testicles.

VI

The apparent success of Voronoff's testicular transplants in the 1920s invites comment. That Voronoff was wrong there is no doubt. Laboratory experiments later confirmed that such gland grafts from one species to another could not succeed. Even grafts between individuals within a species usually fail; and if the grafts had succeeded, and had continued to produce their hormone – testosterone – this does not rejuvenate or increase sexual activity. A grafted gland does not contain any appreciable stores of this hormone; the grafts, even though dead, could not possibly have formed a depot of testosterone for slow release for some time.

There are several possible explanations for Voronoff's self-deception and his patients' approval. Although they are normally thought to be coolly objective people, scientists are in fact frequently misled by their own enthusiasms, and such self-deceptions can arise in a number of ways.

It may seem surprising that so many medical and lay people believed Voronoff, but in the 1920s, it was part of the conventional wisdom that such tissue grafts could succeed. Skin-grafting between unrelated individuals was thought to be possible, perhaps because of the undoubted success with bone and corneal grafts taken from unrelated human donors. And the discovery of blood 'groups', which made possible successful blood transfusion, suggested that tissue grafts could succeed if the same rules were applied, or that transplantation might succeed by chance in a proportion of cases, when the 'groups' happened to fit.

We now know that no sooner had these vessels grown into the graft than the monkey tissue was subjected to a major immunological attack. Transplants to man from animals, including monkeys, are rejected vigorously after the blood vessels grow in. But the effects of this rejection would not be obvious and there would be little general upset. Moreover, the graft would be replaced by the cells causing rejection: it would not disappear, and a lump would remain at the operation site. This nodule sitting on top of the patient's alleged run-down testicle doubtless reassured the patient, and misled Voronoff.

There were only a small number of biologists who knew that success with gland-grafting was unlikely. Some, like Schöne and Lexer in Vienna, had been authorities on the subject of transplantation before the First World War, and had had their scientific environment rudely interrupted by the War. Alexis Carrel also understood before the War that such grafts rejected, but, as we have seen, he seemed uninterested in gland-grafting in the 1920s and devoted his energies instead to tissue-culture – the growth of cells outside the body, usually in animal or human serum. Interestingly he found that old serum was a poor liquid for growth of his cells, but that young serum was a good medium. Carrel considered that young animals had some sort of cell activator, and he may have sympathised with the hunt for rejuvenating hormones. Only late in the day did he speak out against gland-grafting, and then only obliquely. He may have sympathised with Voronoff's battles in Paris with the conservative forces in French science, or perhaps he did not wish to embarrass him publicly.

Voronoff's patients' belief that they had been rejuvenated is perhaps surprising, but easily explained. Throughout the history of medical treatment, large numbers of patients have regularly reported benefits from treatments which could not possibly have worked. This apparent success was either the result of spontaneous improvement of a fluctuating illness or debility or the doctor's enthusiasm and powers of suggestion. Only by the middle of the twentieth century were these pitfalls recognised when judging the effects of treatment in human patients. Thereafter, 'control' groups of untreated patients were used for comparison, and unbiased assessments of the results were adopted in clinical research. Not only were control groups essential, but it was best for the investigator not to know which treatment was in use; and the patients were assigned at random to the treatments.

Voronoff, of course, had no such untreated control groups in his original animal experiments, nor in his human work. Nor did he make any measurements on his patients: 'rejuvenation' was judged subjectively. A man of Voronoff's charismatic personality and considerable presence would have had no difficulty in convincing his patients that they were receiving something of value, especially when the problem treated was something as variable and sensitive to suggestion as general well-being and sexual function. Voronoff's impressive private clinic, the paraphernalia of the operation, in particular the simultaneous surgery on the monkey, would have left a powerful impression on the patient. And no doubt the very considerable fee charged by Voronoff also had a therapeutic effect on the patient: it was unlikely that, whatever his doubts about the effect of the operation, a patient would return home and admit that the trip had been an expensive waste of time. Moreover, Voronoff insisted on a sensible preliminary ritual before the transplant operation took place. He brought the patients into his clinic for one or two weeks in advance, and discouraged or even stopped them from smoking and drinking.

This preliminary time spent in the clinic doubtless had a beneficial effect: his patients were removed from the bustle of normal life for two weeks and forced to abstain from minor vices. Anyone would feel rejuvenated by such a regimen. Voronoff also claimed that the benefits of grafting might not be apparent for some months. This sensible prognostication allowed for spontaneous improvement to occur; it also gave time for cheques to be cashed.

VII

Voronoff's success in attracting patients increased in the 1920s. From a slow start, the number of his gland operations was now rising. By 1922, he had done only twelve: in the year 1923 he performed thirty. By the end of 1926, he reported that he had performed about one thousand gland grafts. If true, this means that he was then carrying out about ten such operations each week, bearing in mind his winter lay-off on the Riviera.

Although the operation was not difficult, this represented a significant work-load: quite apart from anything else, the organisation required to supply the donor monkeys was considerable. Voronoff had no more time for research at the Collège de France, but the authorities seemed unconcerned about this, nor did his publicity seeking appear to worry them.

The work of the rejuvenators was beginning to attract the attention of writers. Steinach was used as a character in Conan Doyle's *The Creeping Man*, and Voronoff may have been portrayed in Mikhail Bulgakov's *The Heart of a Dog*, while Dorothy Sayers used his name sympathetically in *The Unpleasantness at the Bellona Club*. In 1923 the American novelist, Gertrude Atherton, wrote a best-selling novel called *Black Oxen*. Based on the possibility of rejuvenation, it outsold the other 'book of the year', *Gentlemen Prefer Blondes*, and was later made into a highly successful film.

Black Oxen examined one of a number of ethical pseudo-problems which logically followed if the claims for gland grafting were correct. These naive debates directly encouraged a belief in rejuvenation. The novel's theme was the dilemma of a young man who found himself in love with a beautiful woman, who in fact was a rejuvenated seventy-year-old. The rejuvenation method described was that of Steinach, who – as we have seen – as well as offering his vasoligation method for men, used irradiation of the ovaries for female rejuvenation. Gertrude Atherton herself first took this treatment at the age of fifty-six; she died in 1948 at the impressive age of ninety-one. In 1924 she visited Berlin, and suggested that Germany would make herself great again by using rejuvenation methods. Her suggestion excited some comment, if little action, with one paper humorously protesting against the suggestion that the ageing Ludendorff – 'now posing as a great leader' – should be rejuvenated. German interest in the subject soon declined, possibly as a result of the distinguished Professor Hoffmeister claiming, in 1927, that such transplants were not successful. The Third Reich's interest in eugenics may have led to a brief interest in gland transplants, but by then the operation was under suspicion, and the thrust of race improvement under the Nazis was directed along other routes, notably sterilisation and marriage laws.

Another novel in the same genre was *The Gland Stealers* by Bertram

Gayton. It was less serious in tone, and was produced in Britain by the publishers of the novels of P. G. Wodehouse.

The blurb reads thus:

Gran'pa is ninety-five, possessed of £100,000, a fertile imagination, and a good physique. He sees in the papers accounts of Professor Voronoff's theory of rejuvenation by means of gland-grafting.

Nothing will satisfy him but that the experiment should be made upon himself. He acquires a gorilla, a hefty murderous brute, and the operation is performed with success. That is only the beginning.

He next determines to dig out an old love, and make her young too; and Sally, a dear old lady of seventy, arrives upon the scene.

Inspired to philanthropy by the thrill of regained youth, Gran'pa decides to take a hundred or so old men to Africa, capture a like number of gorillas, and borrow their glands.

There are thrilling adventures with the gorillas, whilst the old gentlemen supply the comedy – there are not enough glands to go round. The result of the operations is a surprise to all, particularly to the old gentlemen themselves.

In the end Gran'pa is only temporarily rejuvenated, and accelerated ageing follows; the senior citizens conclude that natural ageing is best, and that modern science should not meddle with nature. This conclusion was to be put forward from more serious sources later.

Other events during 1923 helped to sustain the standing of gland-grafting. The rejuvenated lifers at San Quentin were not forgotten, and at the annual prison Thanksgiving Games in November, the field events proved a newsworthy event. Gland-transplanted inmates did well, and the seventy-year-old John Pearson, who was carrying an extra grafted testicle, came a good second in the fifty-yard dash, beating several younger inmates with only two testicles.

In New York, a surgeon named H. Lyons Hunt reported that he had performed eighty-four gland transplants, using fragments of bull's testicles. He claimed a 90 per cent success rate, including the rejuvenation of a local clergyman and the curing of several male 'perverts'. For most of the operations he had used sheep testicles kept cool in a refrigerator for up to thirty hours. These glands could not possibly have survived for this time. There was more good news for gland graft enthusiasts in early 1924. In January, a Madrid surgeon,

Francisco E. Ortego, reported a successful sheep thyroid gland transplant, which had, the story said, converted an eighteen-year-old mentally defective girl who was under three feet high into a tall statuesque woman. This was impossible.

VII

This confusion and muddle over gland-grafting, so typical of the frothy enthusiasms of the 1920s, was only part of a larger state of confusion in the study of the endocrine glands. The earlier triumph of the discovery of the thyroid extract was followed by the drama involved in the extraction of insulin from the pancreas by Banting in Canada in 1922. Insulin therapy gave remarkable effects, restoring diabetic patients from chronic ill-health to a normal life: diabetics in life-threatening coma were restored to normal health in a couple of hours. Thyroid treatment had been similarly effective in curing cretins and those with myxoedema – thyroid shortage in adult life. The new science of the glands seemed to promise further wonders to come, and it was eagerly assumed that other organs of the body also made hormones with dramatic potential, and many extracts were prepared and sold. This view was only partly correct; none of the hormones later discovered had quite the revolutionary effect on clinical medicine as the thyroid extracts and insulin. In the early 1920s the possibilities for endocrinology seemed endless, and there was a good deal of optimism even in cautious academic circles. Gland grafting seemed a legitimate aspect of such expectations.

Ideas on the role of the endocrine glands went well beyond mere therapeutics. For example, Sir Arthur Keith's otherwise correct and incisive studies of comparative anatomy and the human races were briefly affected by his vague concepts of the roles of the endocrine glands. He proposed that the Negroid facial features resulted from high pituitary activity and that their skin pigment was controlled by the adrenal glands. It made sense, of a sort, but his ideas were soon buried decently.

In private medical practice the new extract therapies not only made sense but good business as well. Pharmaceutical firms enlarged their range of gland extracts to include those of dubious content. Fashionable practitioners diagnosed alleged glandular deficiencies or over-activity which, they claimed, were responsible not only for a mass of trivial unexplained illnesses, but also for personality traits and mental illness. Serious-minded pseudo-scientific textbooks appeared on the glands and glandular therapy – organotherapy – which sold well and led to public debate. The result was that a pseudo-science grew up which, as was said later, threatened to 'strangle endocrinology at birth'. One of its prominent practitioners, Dr Harry Benjamin of New York, could say in a paper to a serious conference:

A person with a constitutionally strong pituitary gland for instance will grow old in a different manner than one in whom this gland has been inferior and the cause of disturbances. And he will also age differently from one with a well balanced thyroid or one with equally well functioning gonads or adrenal glands. Therefore the individualisation of endocrine reactivation-therapy is apparent.

This muddled talk has more in common with Aristotle's humours than twentieth-century medicine: whereas the ancients thought that the sanguine humour controlled ageing, the testis was elevated to the same role by the organotherapists. The bland talk of 'inferior' glands, 'disturbances' in secretion and 'well-balanced' or 'wellfunctioning' glands had a reassuring quality at first, but on closer examination is totally lacking in precision. Benjamin made a fortune in this murky world individualising his treatments for unclear vague diagnoses such as 'disturbed', 'inferior' or indeed the supremely impressive but imprecise diagnosis 'lack of balance' of the endocrine glands. Another such practitioner was Ivo G. Cobb, working on the fringes of Harley Street, who solemnly wrote in a book called *Glands of Destiny* that Napoleon's achievements were the result of early pituitary deficiency, and claimed that Henry VIII had the same plus early thyroid loss. Voltaire, he considered, had powerful adrenal glands.

The birth-pangs of endocrinology were viewed askance by some of the more conventional scientists. The London endocrinologist Professor Swale Vincent constantly called for caution, and in review lectures given on important occasions, he criticised the poor standards of those involved at the frontiers of the new science. Vincent and his supporters condemned two groups:

1. Persons engaged in attempting to cure diseases whose optimism and eagerness to help sway their deficient critical sense until they seize at any straw which seems to point toward success. There is often a love of romance in these people which makes them delight in spinning a misty intellectual mesh which completely obscures any possible facts. This is a large and sincere class, including a mass of general practitioners, most dispensing chemists, a number of consultants, not a few journalists, many medical men.

2. Persons who have realised the commercial possibilities in exploiting the human weakness characteristic of the last-named class. Certain of the firms placing 'endocrine' preparations on the market belong to this last class.

One of the medical men who was chided for a 'love of romance' was Sir Walter Langdon-Brown, who later became Regius Professor of Medicine at Oxford University. Langdon-Brown was in no mood for caution at this time and he in turn criticised Vincent's attitude. Langdon-Brown is remembered for a memorable phrase he introduced in a lecture to the West Kent Medico-Chirurgical Society, in which he said that 'we are marionettes of our glands.' This catchy epigram is uncomfortably close to 'we are as old as our glands', a famous phrase which Brinkley in Kansas claimed to have thought up, and certainly used endlessly. Fashionable practitioners were not prepared to listen to critics like Swale Vincent; as Dr Leonard Williams wrote to the *Lancet* – again from the fringes of Harley Street – listening to one of Vincent's lectures:

Sir,
    Who, I wonder, is profited by Prof. Swale Vincent's periodical scoldings of the clinical endocrinologist? Certainly not the latter, for we, the culprits are serenely impenitent. Almost certainly not the former, because he is depressingly negative. And surely not the medical public, for no public is ever influenced by unconstructive scolding. After all, what does it matter if we do allow our imaginations occasionally to run riot? Endocrinology is still very far from being an exact science, and guesses at the truth are no more reprehensible in this department than they are in any other sphere where experiment and speculation have walked profitably hand in hand. Did bacteriology rise fully equipped out of Pasteur's head, like Athena out of Jupiter's? Or did radiology out of Röntgen's? And if not, are we expected to believe that there were no vain imaginings in the evolution of these sciences?
    Moreover, Prof. Swale Vincent, by his valuable contributions to endocrinology, has done his bit in stimulating that very enthusiasm which he is

now so tireless in rebuking. It is a pity that he should be tiresome as well as tireless. Negative nagging is always a nuisance, but when it proceeds from one who has abundantly proved himself to be capable of better things, it becomes something in the nature of a tragedy.

Swale Vincent was in a minority. Even scientists like Ernest H. Starling and Walter Cannon looked confidently ahead to generalisations on a grand scale and great unifying principles; only their talent for sensing the truth and avoiding error prevented embarrassing claims. Cannon's views of the importance and ramifications of the endocrine glands, popularised in his book *The Wisdom of the Body*, narrowly avoided the excesses which left other, less talented, scientists open to ridicule in hindsight. It is little wonder that the gland-grafters felt safe in their tenets and their claims. They were not only operating at a time of uncertainty about transplantation and immunology: they were also surrounded by endocrinological muddle.

In 1924, the *New York Times* review section contained a series of articles on 'Science promises an Amazing Future', including one on recent advances in the science of glandular secretion. The author was R. G. Hoskins, the editor of the orthodox scientific journal *Endocrinology*. In his list of major achievements in the study of the glands, he highlighted the successful extraction and use of insulin. He then went on to discuss gland transplantation and was cautiously optimistic: 'Some encouraging results have been secured by gland transplants in man. But these are still at an experimental stage . . . the problem of rejuvenation will probably be solved by endocrine research.' That same year the *Scientific American* was also optimistic that glandular research held the key to future miracles: 'Even death, save by accident, may become unknown, if the daring experiments of Dr Serge Voronoff, brilliant French surgeon, continue to produce results such as have startled the world.'

It's hardly surprising that Van Buren Thorne's book review of a popular work on the glands, Benjamin Harrow's *Glands and Health and Disease*, should wearily conclude that 'a war-ridden world has given place to a gland-ridden world. We have been Voronoffed and Steinached – Brinkleyed too – until a long-suffering public is really in doubt as to whether world comity or the world's glandular condition should occupy first place.'

Gland-grafting and organotherapy, though controversial and criticised, were seen by many as two of the most exciting growth points in medicine and surgery. As usual, moderate men listened charitably to the claims, and many believed that results would improve as the science and surgical methods became more sophisticated. The cautious leader writer of the moderate *Boston Medical and Surgical Journal* wrote:

Like any new operations, testicular transplantation will have to pass first through a period in which it will be desired by the neurotic and the overstimulated. In many such cases its results will probably be unsuccessful. Its employment will be checked, fortunately, by the difficulty in obtaining material for transplantation. Later on, it will be adopted by the more conservative surgeons as a legitimate means of therapeusis in certain well-defined types of cases. Just what these will be, can only be learned by experience.

At any rate, a new chapter in surgery and physiology is being written. It will be surprising if, from this most interesting field of experimentation, something of value is not obtained for mankind.

VIII

In fact nothing of any value was obtained for mankind – not even the salutary lesson that medical science can err at times, since the whole gland-grafting affair was later dismissed as quackery. One further unpleasant lesson of value could have been learned, and was probably becoming obvious in the secret world of Voronoff's private practice. Monkey tissue can transmit several serious diseases: Voronoff's patients were being exposed to venereal disease, tuberculosis and some particularly nasty viruses. But Voronoff's work was outside any scrutiny, and he was committed to a public stance of boundless confidence. The dangers of monkey tissue had to be learned again by others.

In 1924 a compliment to Voronoff came from an unimpeachable source – the Royal College of Surgeons of England. Each year, one of their most important events is the series of Hunterian Lectures given by distinguished surgeons and medical men who are asked to address themselves to important contemporary themes. In 1924 the lecturers included Alexander Fleming, later to discover penicillin, and the distinguished surgeon W. Heneage Ogilvie. That February the lecturer was the London surgeon Kenneth M. Walker FRCS, the surgeon in charge of the genito-urinary departments at the Royal Northern Hospital and the Miller General Hospital for South-East London. Walker chose 'Testicular Grafts' as his subject. In his introduction he had no difficulty connecting his theme with the work of John Hunter, as is traditional on these occasions. As we have seen, the great eighteenth-century surgeon and experimentalist had himself experimented with transplantation using hens and cocks, and had carried out testis transplants. His claims for successful testicle and ovary grafts were well-known and his reports had a powerful and unfortunate effect on those interested in transplantation over the next 150 years. Hunter's successful grafting experiments are partly unexplained, but some of the causes for his self-deception are clear. He worked in the era before microscopy, and could only judge the 'success' of his grafts by the fact that some tissue remained visible at the graft site. This may only have been scar tissue. The second source of error was that the animal's own glands may have been incompletely removed, and tiny extra bits of gland had enlarged to restore the secretion.

Walker's introduction used Hunter's experiments to show that gland grafting had ancient, respectable origins. He then described how he personally had experimented on human patients, firstly with a testicular extract, and that although he obtained some good results, 'in none of these cases have I been able to convince myself that this was not the result of mental suggestion.' Walker's admission that spurious therapeutic success could be obtained by auto-suggestion showed him to be a careful investigator, and indeed awareness of the power of suggestion was increasing in the 1920s. Walker then turned to the question of testis grafting, and described how impressed he was by the results reported by L. L. Stanley on the gland grafts of San Quentin. He also acknowledged the lead given by Serge Voronoff.

Walker went on to give an account, in great clinical detail, of ten cases of human testicular grafting. In six of these he claimed success. He had used human testis for the graft, obtaining slices taken from 'ectopic' human testes – in other words, glands which have to be removed from other patients because of their wrong position. He hinted that he thought monkey testicle grafts might also work, though he had not tried them. His conclusions were cautious. In spite of his six good results, he felt that his grafts might last only two years. Moreover, he believed that transplantation was merely a temporary measure to be used until the testis hormone was discovered and extracted: 'However brilliant the results that the implantation of a testicular graft may sometimes give, it is obvious that severe limitations are imposed . . . and as was the case in the organotherapy of the thyroid, but little advance will be made until the use of grafts is replaced by that of a really efficient extract.' Walker's lecture received favourable comment in an editorial in the *British Medical Journal*.

Thus, at least three surgeons in London were active in carrying out gland transplantations – Ivor Back of St George's, Walker of the Royal Northern and a third, Norman Haire, who that year published a book entitled *Rejuvenation*. Haire was a London medical man of slightly mysterious background living at 90 Harley Street, and had contributed articles about rejuvenation, sexual hygiene, and race purity to the popular press.

In Russia, the talented Professor Shamov took an interest briefly, while in Italy there was intense interest in Voronoff's work and Dr Ettore Mariotto claimed, correctly, to have preceded him in performing a testis transplant. Support for Voronoff was evident in medical articles from throughout Italy, and particularly from the South. Dr Salvatore Fici of Palermo confirmed Voronoff's successful use of testis grafts, as did Professor Nicola Pende of Cagliari, who suggested that multiple endocrine organ transplants might be even more successful. Some Italian academics were more cautious. Professor N. Leotta of the University of Bari felt that the action of testicle grafts faded in time, and such grafts simply acted as a depot of hormone.

IX

About this time, Voronoff published his second monograph, *Quarante-trois Greffes du Singe à l'Homme*. It was an updated account of his personal testis transplant experience, now totalling forty-three grafts. The *British Medical Journal* reviewed it: if this journal had been neutral the previous year, it now was enthusiastic about Voronoff's operation, and a long review was published:

Dr Voronoff has been the victim of a certain amount of misrepresentation and prejudice, largely owing to the premature interest which the lay press has taken in his work. It is work, of course, which must tickle the fancy of laymen, and is in its broad outline easily understandable by them. No doubt the use of monkey tissue for the rejuvenation of men – a return, as it were, to our ancestry for refreshment – has in it certain elements of humour which have not passed unrecognized. Judging Dr Voronoff's work by his paper in London before the Congrès International de Chirurgie last year, and by this book, one must concede at once his honesty of purpose. We must apologize for having raised that point, but we think it well to do so in face of the prejudices which have greeted him . . .

We must admit after reading this book that the testicular graft is something worthy of serious consideration. It is for this reason that we have given so much space to the notice of the book. Certain opinions of a condemnatory nature are current in medical circles – opinions founded on hearsay without full knowledge of the facts. Dr Voronoff has set forth his views without exaggeration. He is, of course, an enthusiast, but he is an enthusiast who honestly admits his failures, and more than that we have no right to demand of him. The true place in therapeusis of testicular grafts will be decided not by Dr Voronoff, but by the future experiences of our profession with the method . . .

The Lancet also reviewed the book, but was more cautious: the writer suggested that Voronoff's work was not yet needed on every book-shelf.

In 1925, an English translation of this monograph became available in a translation by Fred F. Imianintoff B.A. (Lond.) entitled *Rejuvenation by Grafting*. The *Lancet* continued to maintain its careful attitude. In a half-column review in March 1925, it summarised the book, and the reviewer concluded cautiously: 'The book is written by an enthusiast and there are some statements within its covers which cannot be accepted without reserve. However, it must be admitted that Dr Voronoff has accumulated a great deal of material in support of this thesis, and for this reason the work merits attention.'

In 1926 Voronoff produced yet another book. In his *Étude sur la Vieillesse et la Rajeunessement par la Greffe* he went over much of the same ground as before, but added a preliminary chapter on the general biology of ageing. It was published in Britain as *The Study of Old Age and My Method of Rejuvenation.* The *British Medical Journal* enthused about it in a review, not only acclaiming Voronoff's results but also praising him personally. The *Lancet* also reviewed the new book but continued to be cautious, and was critical of some deficiencies:

Interesting as is 'The Study of Old Age' it cannot be perused without a feeling of disappointment at the method of presentation. We hear too much of the author's successes and too little of his failures. No attempt has been made to analyse the thousand cases of animal grafting and the 600 human experiments and tabulate the results. In how many of the cases were the results negative? . . . Voronoff has contented himself with subjective evidence supplemented by the evidence of the camera. He writes for the public rather than for the scientist . . .

But such quibbles were easily shrugged off by the testis transplant enthusiasts. If Voronoff was at all discouraged by the *Lancet's* criticisms, his confidence must have been boosted by other invitations, in particular an invitation to write the entry on 'Rejuvenation' for the 1926 edition of the *Encyclopaedia Britannica*. In the contributors' list for that volume he was listed, as usual, as Director of the Physiological Station of the Collège de France and as a teacher at l'École des Hautes Études. To write such an article is, for a professional scientist, a tedious chore lightened by the eventual receipt of a small fee. But Voronoff must have been delighted to go over the arguments in favour of the idea of control of ageing by the testis, and to summarise the alleged success of his testis transplants for this prestigious international publication.

x

In the mid-1920s Voronoff's activities were always news, and he was always ready to talk about his plans for future work. He was increasingly patronised by the rich and famous, and was a favourite medical celebrity with the newspapers. In one of a number of such Voronoff stories it was announced that the great gland surgeon was, unexpectedly, taking a cruise in the Mediterranean on his yacht. Soon afterwards came news that the Premier of Turkey, Mustapha Kemel Pasha, was holidaying in the southern Turkish town of Adana. The newspapers soon confirmed from 'reliable sources' in

Paris that the frail Turkish Premier had been gland-grafted by Voronoff.

At this time Voronoff received a number of conventional honours. He was awarded a number of decorations in France, including the Legion of Honour, and in Spain he was awarded the Order of Elisabeth. While visiting and grafting in South-East Asia, he collected a Commandership of the Dragon of Vietnam and the Grand Cross of the Royal Order of Cambodia; and in Italy he was made a Grand Officer of the Crown. His assistant, Dr Dartigues, received the Léon Labbé Prize of the French Academy of Medicine for his work on testis transplants. In 1926 Voronoff himself set up a prize for research on the endocrine glands, with a value of 10,000 francs (about £500). The Russian-born surgeon inserted a curious restriction on those eligible for the prize: it was to be awarded only to those of the Latin race and having a 'Latin mentality'.

Perhaps the ultimate compliment to Voronoff followed in 1927, when he announced that a Hungarian insurance company had refused to pay out an old-age annuity to one of his testis-grafted patients. The company stated that the beneficial effects of the operation had been established scientifically and that the transplanted patient was younger than his chronological age; hence they no longer considered that the contract was valid.

1. Serge Voronoff in middle age.

2. Serge Voronoff as depicted in the gossipy Paris magazine *Chanteclair* in 1910. He is shown as a surgeon operating to remove an appendix; the themes in the background refer to his earlier activities and publications in Egypt.

3. The *New York Times* reports on Voronoff's activities in 1914.

BONE GRAFTING IN ARMY.

Dr. Voronoff Applies Carrel Method and Saves Soldier's Arm.

Special Cable to THE NEW YORK TIMES.

PARIS, Dec. 3.—The Russian surgeon, Dr. Voronoff, who, with Dr. Alexis Carrel, discovered the method of bone grafting in the Rockefeller Institute for Medical Research in New York, today announced the first successful application of the method in the case of a wounded soldier at the Russian hospital in Bordeaux. The operation consisted of the transplantation of a piece of bone from a monkey's arm to replace a splinter carried away by a shell.

4. An old ram used in Voronoff's 1918 experiments, after testis grafting.
Holding the ram is Voronoff's assistant and future wife,
the rich Standard Oil heiress, Evelyn Bostwick.

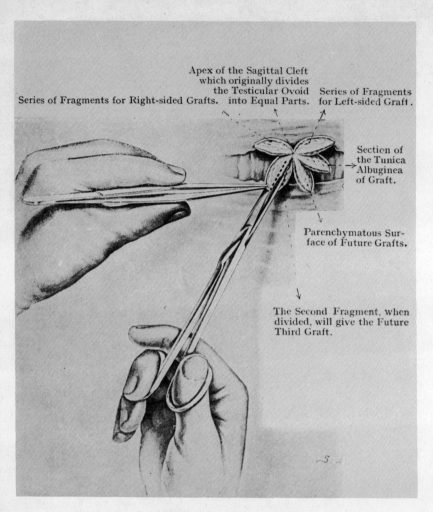

Apex of the Sagittal Cleft
which originally divides
the Testicular Ovoid
Series of Fragments for Right-sided Grafts.   into Equal Parts.

Series of Fragments
for Left-sided Graft.

Section of
the Tunica
Albuginea
of Graft.

Parenchymatous Sur-
face of Future Grafts.

The Second Fragment, when
divided, will give the Future
Third Graft.

5. The surgical technique for removing the gland-graft slices
from the donor monkey.

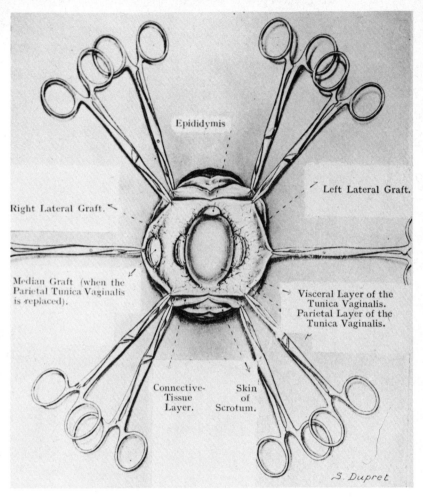

Epididymis

Left Lateral Graft.

Right Lateral Graft.

Median Graft (when the
Parietal Tunica Vaginalis
is replaced).

Visceral Layer of the
Tunica Vaginalis.
Parietal Layer of the
Tunica Vaginalis.

Connective-
Tissue
Layer.

Skin
of
Scrotum.

S. Dupret

6. Voronoff's surgical technique of testis-grafting, in which slices of donor
monkey testis were stitched on to the recipient's own testis.

7. Edward Liardet, one of Voronoff's monkey gland transplant recipients, demonstrating his new vitality after the operation. He testified for Voronoff during the controversy of 1922.

THE GLAND STEALERS

Bertram Gayton

8. The jacket of a popular novel inspired k
activities of the monkey gland transplante

LEFT: *Senile, feeble and decrepit: A twelve-year-old ram before being grafted.* RIGHT: *The same old ram almost six years later, with his mate and third lamb*

Can Old Age Be Deferred?

An Interview with Dr. Serge Voronoff, the Famous Authority on the Possibilities of Gland Transplantation

THERE is a "Fountain of Eternal Youth." It lies in your glands. Through its life-giving flow old age may be postponed, if not avoided. Even death, save by accident, may become unknown, if the daring experiments of Dr. Serge Voronoff, brilliant French surgeon, continue to produce results such as have startled the world.

"My first determination to undertake this work," said Dr. Voronoff, "came from the realization of the dominant role of the endocrine glands in the human organism. Up to forty or fifty years ago physicians admitted that the energy which caused our organs to perform their various functions was an inherent one. They took it more or less for granted, however, that the secret of this energy never would be found—that the inherent energy that made the heart beat, for example, was a God-given motive power not to be tampered with."

Brain Not the Controlling Center of Life

These theories, Dr. Voronoff pointed out, were first shattered by the remarkable experiments and discoveries of Claude Bernard on the endocrinal value of the liver. Close on the heels of Bernard's research came the work of Brown-Sequard. For the first time the brain was found to be not the controlling center of life, but a peculiar combination of gray flesh, capable of producing thought only when properly controlled by the chemical action of the liquid from the thyroid glands.

With improper functioning of this gland a young man became mentally old and feeble, useless to himself and to society. His physical condition, too, formerly strong and healthy, became weak and unsteady. Infants with congenital atrophy of the thyroid always show, both mentally and physically, the effects of such a condition, being puny in every way. Animals deprived of their thyroid glands soon after birth, according to experiments, are altogether outgrown by others of the same age within a period of eight to ten months.

On the other hand, it has been proved by experiment that a hypertrophy, or over-development, of the thyroid gland will cause such an over-excitation of the mental processes as to amount in some cases almost to insanity. Hypertrophy of other glands, such as the pituitary glands, which are situated at the base of the brain and which control the growth of the living cells, will cause occasional freak giants.

"Even the smallest glands sometimes play the largest roles," observed Dr. Voronoff. "Take away from an animal the four little para-thyroids, located beside the thyroid, and the effect is absolutely disastrous. The nervous system undergoes a terrific over-excitation, the muscles contract violently, and the subject dies in violent convulsions within a short time. The suprarenal glands, if removed, will cause death by a sort of strange lethargy, known as Addison's disease.

"But," continued the great surgeon, "it is, after all, the functions of the reproductive gland that have taken my entire attention since 1910.

"This remarkable and all important center, which has been regarded until recently as merely a mechanism for the prolongation of the life of the race on earth, plays one of the greatest and most important parts in our everyday normal physical existence."

Dr. Voronoff pointed to the many examples of men and animals deprived of these glands. Their flesh becomes soft and flabby. Their mental energy wanes; their whole bodies sag and drop out of proper form; their blood is thin and poor. From latest observations it is entirely probable, says the doctor, that the work of the other glands may be distinctly affected and reduced by the loss of the secretions of these central glands.

As one remarkable example of the opposite effects caused by the over-development of the gland in question, Doctor Voronoff cited the case of a boy nine years old who was suffering from a hypertrophy of one genital gland. He had a full black beard and mustache, remarkably hairy arms and legs and the stockily settled appearance of a mature, though small man. When the extra growth was removed, the boy lost, within six months, all of his beard except his mustache, as well as the heavy hair on his arms and legs. His mental condition, which previously had been far above normal for his age, dropped back nearly to that of other boys of his own years.

Results Not Immediate

"Here," said Doctor Voronoff, "was a remarkable demonstration that the glands play a part of primary importance in our mental and physical development. This does not mean that it is always the amount of glandular tissue present which can be called a hypertrophy, but it is evident from present knowledge of the construction of the glandular system that an over-growth makes itself felt upon the entire human system."

First attempts to change the conditions of men from this source were made, according to Dr. Voronoff, in 1869, when Brown-Sequard endeavored to inject into the glandular tissue of a man secretions from the glands of an animal. The experiment was successful at first, but the effects did not last for any length of time.

The experiment proved one thing, however—which is known also from other investigations—that the glandular secretions of both man and animal are chemically identical. The reactions observed are brought about, not through the energy of the fluid, but rather through the quality of the organism upon which the fluid acts. The thyroid gland of a man grafted into a sheep could not produce the mental activity of the man in the lower animal, nor

DR. SERGE VORONOFF
Well-known exponent of rejuvenation by gland-grafting

9. Voronoff and his wife shown at work in a laudatory article in the *Scientific American* of October 1925.

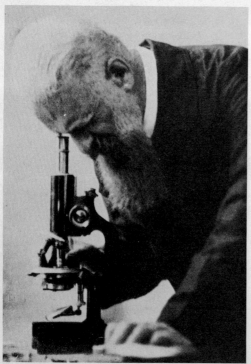

10. Professor Steinach and his research group outside the Vivarium in Vienna in 1922. Included in the group are Kammerer and Koppanyi, both of whose suspect biological work was criticised later.

11. Professor Steinach.

12. Campaign stamps used by Brinkley in his gubernatorial contest in Kansas – one of many novelties used by Brinkley during his campaign.

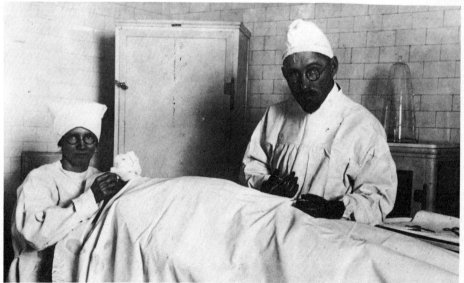

13. A puff from the *New York Evening Journal* praising 'Doc' Brinkley's work. Brinkley's wife is on the right, while he is shown holding the first 'goat gland baby', born to one of his goat testis gland recipients.

14. Dr John R. Brinkley with his wife in the laboratory which they established at the Brinkley-Jones Hospital in Milford, Kansas.

15. The international delegation which visited Algeria to study Voronoff's testis-graft experiments in sheep. Voronoff is the tall figure in the centre. The leader of the British delegation, F.A.E. Crew of Edinburgh, is in the plus-fours.

MINISTRY OF AGRICULTURE AND FISHERIES

BOARD OF AGRICULTURE FOR SCOTLAND

Report

ON

Dr. Serge Voronoff's Experiments

ON THE

IMPROVEMENT OF LIVESTOCK

By

F. H. A. MARSHALL, Sc.D., F.R.S.,
F. A. E. CREW, M.D., D.Sc., Ph.D.,
A. WALTON, Ph.D., and
Wm. C. MILLER, M.R.C.V.S.

LONDON:
PUBLISHED BY HIS MAJESTY'S STATIONERY OFFICE.
To be purchased directly from H.M. STATIONERY OFFICE at the following addresses:
Adastral House, Kingsway, London, W.C.2; 120, George Street, Edinburgh;
York Street, Manchester; 1, St. Andrew's Crescent, Cardiff;
15, Donegall Square West, Belfast;
or through any Bookseller.

1928

Price 9d. Net.

24—108.

16. Title page of the cautious British report on Voronoff's Algerian experiments.

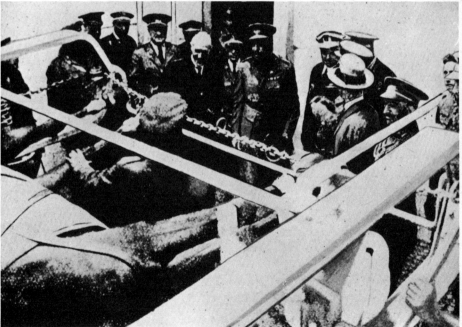

17. (*above*) The Algerian Government's exhibit at the 1931 International Colonial Exhibition in Paris. The grafted sheep are shown on the left, and have obviously heavier weights and better wool than the normal animals on the right. This was the last appearance of the discredited experiments.

18. (*below*) A view of the testis graft carried out on a horse belonging to the King of Spain in 1927. The King personally attended the operation.

19. Paul Niehans shown outside his private rejuvenation clinic in Switzerland. Niehans reputation rose after the fall of Voronoff.

V
HUBRIS: THE YEARS
OF SUCCESS

Voronoff's successful defence of his gland operation, and the growing interest of others in his surgical *méthode*, gave rise to a new problem – that of to ensuring a reliable and adequate supply of monkeys as donors. These animals were obtained specially for his work and came largely from the African colonies belonging to Spain and Belgium.

As Voronoff increased the number of monkeys brought from Africa to meet the needs of his surgical practice, he decided to establish a holding area for the animals in the Riviera, and proposed to breed them there as well. The French authorities, however, refused him permission to breed monkeys, so instead he purchased the huge Château Grimaldi, just across the Italian border at Ventimiglia on the Italian Riviera. This became his winter home, which he shared with his brother Alexandre. There were extensive grounds round the Château and in them he set up a secure monkey colony. He engaged a professional animal-keeper, Charles Bartell, a Dutchman who had formerly been in circus work. At the height of Voronoff's fame in the late 1920s, the Château grounds held fifty monkeys. But to Voronoff's disappointment, the animals did not breed well in captivity. Many also died on their way to this Riviera colony, and many of the survivors must have been diseased.

Monkeys from Africa were used not only for Voronoff's work, but also for conventional medical research. In Paris, the Pasteur Institute also required increasing numbers of monkeys, and Voronoff successfully turned his publicity efforts towards banning the use of monkeys for reasons other than medical research and treatment. He campaigned against the use of monkey skin for clothing or decoration, and his propaganda may have been important in altering public opinion in favour of such a ban.

In 1922 the Pasteur Institute had sent a Dr Wilbert out to West Africa to try to establish a reservation for apes, and so increase the supply to meet the demands of medical research. The impending shortage of monkeys also aroused interest at an earlier stage among entrepreneurs. The *Chicago Tribune* announced on 22 October 1922 that a syndicate was being formed to organise an African expedition to round up chimpanzees, and so corner the market, but nothing more was heard of it.

The French Government also responded at an early stage to such pressure and acted to conserve the monkey supply. In September 1923, the Governor of French West Africa, M. Garde, issued an 'Arrêté' – a decree – to reserve the animals for strictly medical purposes. The monkeys could only be captured by those with a permit issued by the Governor-General, and these permits would only be given for obtaining monkeys for medical research. The killing of monkeys for their skins was banned. Similar moves were made in the Belgian Congo. In his publications Voronoff made much of this new attitude to conservation and he praised these governments. He may have exaggerated the role he played, and it may be that the French Government acted mainly to preserve the supply for the Pasteur Institute. But there is evidence to suggest that in French political circles Voronoff was now an important figure, and becoming more so.

It may be that Voronoff was being used as a symbol of the vitality of post-war French science and medicine. As we have seen, the European countries had lost their former authority in the field of medical research, and the French Government may well have supported him in order to encourage a new confidence in French medicine. Such scientific chauvinism was reflected in differing attitudes to rejuvenation, particularly in the choice between Voronoff and Steinach. Austria and Germany supported Steinach's ligation operation: France backed Voronoff's gland transplant. Britain, if anything, favoured Voronoff, though he was shunned by serious scientists and his clinical imitators were thwarted by the anti-vivisection movement: all the same, his books were favourably reviewed in English language journals, and Voronoff said that the greatest number of the patients who came to him from outside France were English. The Latin races and nations, including the South Americans, were enthusiastic about the prospect of rejuvenation, but elsewhere interest was patchy. American medical men were curious about and used both methods, and particularly around Chicago there was intense interest in gland grafting. However, in New York, Steinach had a noisy supporter – Harry Benjamin of the Life Extension Institute. Benjamin continued to advocate Steinach's vasoligation method for many years and wrote introductions to translations of European texts on rejuvenation. American support for Steinach's operation also came from experiments on American prisoners, similar to the monkey gland operations. A Dr Sharpe of the Indiana State Penitentiary reported that he had carried out the bilateral vasoligation on 456 inmates as a eugenic measure. These sterilised men reported that they were in better health after the operation, and had 'sunnier dispositions'.

Voronoff was generous about his European rival. It might have been expected that Voronoff would be scathing in private, or in public, about Steinach's method, especially since Voronoff's publications state that many of his patients had previously had a Steinach operation without success, but he was consistently polite about Steinach, and in his memoirs Thorek confirms that privately Voronoff was charitable towards him.

However, Steinach was invariably disparaging about his rival's methods. Of Voronoff's work, he said 'it must be emphatically declared that it amounts to self-delusion if people seriously believe that the transplantation of chimpanzee testicles into human beings can produce anything but rapidly passing effects.'

I

In 1925 Voronoff travelled to French West Africa. The *New York Times* told of his travels through Senegal, the Sudan and the Upper Volta. At Kindia, in French Guinea, he demonstrated his method of gland-grafting in a laboratory of the Pasteur Institute building; the demonstration was witnessed by the Governor, himself a medical man. Voronoff then graciously endowed the unit with 100,000 francs to enable them to build a monkey menagerie. Voronoff had a number of reasons for undertaking this trip. He was interested in any means of increasing the supply of monkeys; but – as we shall see– he also had a new and exciting North Africa venture to announce to the world. It was one which was to cause major difficulties for him later on.

He had already reported, two years earlier, that one of the effects of his original experiments on old rams at the Collège de France was that they showed an increased growth of wool. One year later, in 1924, he repeated this claim at a medical congress in Liège, in Belgium. By this time, he had realised, or had had it pointed out to him, that such stimulation of wool growth would have considerable commercial implications, and at the congress he was able to announce that larger scale gland-grafting experiments had started in the French colony of Algeria, using 3,000 sheep in a study of wool growth and breeding. In this he was encouraged by the Governor General of Algeria, Mr. Steeg, and the head of the Department of Sheep Raising, Professor Trouette.

Voronoff had first visited Algeria in 1924. The breeding of the prize bull belonging to the Algerian Agricultural Society was causing concern; Voronoff had been contacted, and after visiting and examining the bull, he had recommended a testis transplant. He had grafted the bull at the Bou Ghellel farm in the spring of that year using the testicles from a two-year old native bull. The operation was done under local anaesthetic and Jacky, the bull, was held down by five Arab assistants. Six months later, Jacky was reported to have revived physically, with his fertility restored. His breeding declined again three years later, and Voronoff operated once more: six months later, further 'rejuvenation' was reported. These claims were to be criticised later, but they meant that Voronoff was well-known in agricultural circles in Algeria, and so obtained facilities for his sheep experiment.

His aim was to gland-graft young sheep and then study their wool production and breeding; and his trip to French West Africa in 1925 was not only to investigate the supply of monkeys, but to expand and continue his experiments on the production of 'super sheep'. His aim, as he told the press at Dakar, was to transform French West

Africa into a vast sheep-raising country. The native sheep were small and stunted: he planned to graft several hundred animals and return next winter to assess and continue the work. And, he claimed, he had already had success with grafting sheep in Tunis.

This was an important claim. It also had major implications, since inspection of Voronoff's human graft work was not possible and the results reported by him from his private transplants had to be taken on trust. But his work with livestock was open to inspection and scrutiny, unhindered by questions of privacy or confidentiality. Moreover, the funding of this sheep transplant work came from government sources, and governments require objective reports and an eventual return on their investment.

The experiments on sheep continued between the years 1924 and 1928. Voronoff must have been busy, dividing his time between the private clinics in Paris, his Riviera retreat, and the breeding station in Algeria. It was a time of consolidation as far as his human transplant technique was concerned, and he operated frequently. He stopped writing about these methods and gave no more results: he no longer spoke regularly at important medical meetings, though he continued to attend. Perhaps he was too busy to contribute, but it is also clear that he had little extra to add to his original reports, and that the sheep experiments were of increasing importance to him, particularly since he thought they amounted to a new and exciting addition to the gland-graft story. And, as a wealthy man, he could indulge himself, causing a stir in the antique-collecting world by purchasing most of the contents of the château of the Comtesse de Behangue: two tapestries alone, one Gobelins and the other from Beauvais by Boucher, were auctioned to him for one million francs.

II

The middle 1920s were also a time of success for John R. Brinkley, and his goat-gland transplants in rural Kansas. After his rebuff by the conventional testis-transplanters of Chicago in 1920, he had returned to the small town of Milford and built up an impressive private medical clinic.

Brinkley turned his considerable talents to devising ways of getting round the disadvantages of his remote situation. His solution was a novel one: he built a radio station. In 1923, when broadcasting was in its infancy and the technology involved was difficult, he succeeded in building and operating one of the most powerful stations in America, KFKB – 'Kansas First, Kansas Best'. In favourable conditions, the 1,000 watt station could be heard in mid-Atlantic. At the time there was no control of broadcasting, and Brinkley was free to do as he wished on the air. Soon Milford had a small community of professional broadcasters, including musicians, preachers and eventually an eleven-piece orchestra. Brinkley himself lectured nightly on current affairs and medical matters. For his mid-west listeners he affected a folksy anti-authority stance. This contrasted with his private persona: he had a sharp mind and in his later legal battles he revealed a mastery of technical detail.

Soon he was advertising his pharmaceuticals on the radio. But the recurrent theme of his medical broadcasts was the need for older men to restore their virility by his goat-gland transplant method. At the height of his success, the post brought letters for medical advice at a rate of 3,000 per day from Kansas, Nebraska, Iowa, Missouri and Oklahoma. It took a substantial staff to deal with this post. If no response was obtained to his first reply, he used increasingly high-pressure salesmanship thereafter, pestering his potential clients remorselessly. If anyone ridiculed him or reneged on payments, he sent in a heavy squad of bullies to discourage them. Almost the entire population of Milford was now working for him. The town was expanding, and this success was based on Brinkley's entrepreneurial skills.

We know something of the hospital routine from the testimony of patients at Brinkley's trial in 1930 for the revocation of his licence. By 1924, the hospital had fifty beds. Patients coming for goat-gland surgery arrived by the Sunday train to Junction City and bus to Milford. On arrival, one of Brinkley's four assistant surgeons examined the patients and did laboratory tests. Late on Sunday evening, and often late at night, Mrs Brinkley visited each new patient and took from them the $750 fee. Little sympathy was shown to those who could not raise the cash immediately or who could not make a convincing case for credit or produce collateral.

However, at Brinkley's trial numerous patients spoke not only of the success of their operation, but also of the efficiency of the hospital and the kindness of the staff. Other types of surgery were carried out, but goat-gland work predominated. Certainly, the pictures of Dr Brinkley at work and the design of his operation room suggest facilities which were advanced for the times. A visiting surgeon reported that the hospital was well equipped and the nursing standards high. He was intrigued to see earphones at each bed, and Brinkley's hospital may have been the first in the world to provide radio for all patients – his own KFKB. However, he thought that Brinkley's own surgical technique was poor, and that the assistant in theatre that day was more skilful.

Patients who took longer than usual to recover from surgery were transferred from the hospital to the local hotel, also owned by Brinkley, so making way for the new batch of Sunday arrivals. Though opponents of Brinkley made much of occasional cases of wound infection or wound breakdown which occurred after his operation, these complications are inevitable in a proportion of such surgery, even in the best of hands. There is no evidence that he was negligent or dangerous in his technique: the clinic was an impressive organisation.

Brinkley's supply of donor testis glands posed no problems. He must have been the first, and perhaps the last, transplant surgeon to have unlimited supplies of donor tissue, and he was shipping in about twenty-five young goats per week. The goats were kept in an open pen two blocks from the hospital, and the patients could hear them bleating.

Brinkley was secretive about his technique, and did not encourage professional visitors to his hospital. His promotional literature gives little detail of his surgical operation, other than to praise it and hint at its complexity. However, at the time of the Kansas State Board's action against him to remove his licence, he not only gave details of his operation, but the Court adjourned to watch a demonstration of the procedure. Brinkley offered a range of operations at various prices. His 'Four-phase Compound Operation' was the most expensive ($750) and the cheaper operations were merely a part of his larger procedure. Though he used goat glands regularly, he offered human testis grafts at $2,000, using a gland 'guaranteed free of disease'. There is little to suggest that he carried out any such human gland transplants regularly.

The 'four-phase' operation consisted of implantation of the gland, ligation of the vas, and attachment of an artery and nerve. Though Brinkley's methods are poorly described, it appears that he did not expose the testis in the same way as Voronoff. It is more likely that he made an incision higher up, near the groin, and placed the graft near the spermatic cord. It is also likely that he used an entire goat testicle as a graft, rather than slices. The testis in the goat is fairly small.

Brinkley's higher incision allowed him access to the duct from the testis – the vas deferens – as it exited from the testis. He divided this, as in the Steinach operation, and the modern vasectomy. At this point, Brinkley did an odd thing: he injected mercurochrome – an antiseptic – up the proximal end of the cut vas deferens. The declared reason for this was to clear any infection from the seminal vesicles, near the prostate gland. Brinkley probably had other reasons. This injection of mercurochrome had an impressive effect on the patient, since it passed from the vas to the seminal vesicles and then to the bladder, and for the next few days the patient's urine was deeply coloured by the antiseptic. This must have helped the mystique of the procedure.

The last frill added to the transplant by Brinkley was one he made much of in his promotional literature. He claimed that he could improve the blood supply and the secretion of the patient's own testis by attaching to it an extra artery and nerve. He argued that, firstly, the new vessel gave extra nourishment, and secondly, that the extra nerve impulses energised the gland. During the operation he searched for and found a small artery and nerve in the adjacent tissues and swung them over, attaching them crudely to the outside of the patient's testicle. Neither of these procedures could have worked or had any influence on the testicles' function. The blood supply, even of the elderly testis, is adequate: the nerve supply to the testis plays no part in its secretion.

Brinkley probably operated only on one side. He divided the vas deferens only on one side. If this had been carried out on both sides, the patient would have become sterile. His mid-western country folk were as much interested in renewed fertility as in potency. In

Europe, perhaps, it was the other way round.

It is not clear whether Brinkley grafted one or two goat glands to each patient: on the basis of the number of goats used, it would appear – at very most – he performed between twenty-five and fifty gland operations a week, a figure also suggested by the fifty beds at the hospital. This would have brought in an income from this source alone of up to $37,000 a week, to which was added his income from radio prescribing. He was soon to be extraordinarily wealthy, eventually owning numerous homes, a fleet of cars, two aeroplanes and a yacht with a large crew. Like Voronoff, Brinkley was successfully consolidating his fame in a climate of opinion which conceded that such testis grafts might work. He treated some distinguished patients: Harry Chandler, the jaded editor of the *Los Angeles Times* was gland-grafted amid great publicity, as were some of his staff. J. J. Tobias, Chancellor of the Chicago Law School, also had the operation, and some time after it he gave an ecstatic press conference in praise of Brinkley.

In 1925 Brinkley attempted to gain some further respectability. Cruising in the Mediterranean, he visited Pavia University in Italy. With an American letter of introduction which listed his early, dubious medical degrees, he was allowed to apply for the Pavia degree of Doctor of Medicine. This ancient university had old regulations which allowed established practitioners to obtain this post-graduate degree as an extra, almost honorary, award. The candidate had to prove his competence by presenting a short thesis and submitting to an oral examination by the professors. A fee was taken by each professor involved. Brinkley enjoyed the little circuit of oral examinations and was delighted to find that one examiner, Professor Parroncito, had himself been gland-grafted recently by Voronoff. Brinkley passed the tests and got his doctorate. Armed with this, he joined the British Medical Association on the way home to America. Back home, he could now claim to have a genuine M.D. degree from an ancient university, and though it was a post-graduate one, it was easily confused with the M.D. degree given to undergraduates by American medical schools. Until the Pavia degree was taken from him in 1927, it was to be a great source of pride to the Kansas testis transplanter.

III

Unlike Voronoff, 'Dr' J. R. Brinkley was clearly a quack. His medical training was suspect, and he eagerly accumulated impressive but dubious qualifications. Itinerant in the early and late parts of his career, he was secretive and did not encourage inspection of his work; nor did he publish descriptions of his methods in medical journals for others to study. He made a conspicuous display of his services, not only by radio, but also by his flashy way of life. He used testimonials extensively, and sought and enjoyed publicity. His goat gland transplants were promoted as a panacea for many ills, and when conventional opinion turned against gland transplantation in the late 1920s he shifted ground and instead advised a modified operation for prostatic enlargement. He was keen to make money; he was also constantly at war with the conventional medical establishment. Lastly, like most quacks, there is little evidence that Brinkley believed in his own goat gland transplants.

If one examines Voronoff's career, a quite different picture emerges. The main complaint against him – that he was wrong, and that his monkey gland transplants were ineffective – is irrelevant: medical sciences frequently make such wrong turnings. His exclusion from the Congress of French Surgeons in 1922 was the result of a personal feud within the Congress, a reproof of his publicity-seeking rather than a criticism of his work, and he and his assistants were made welcome at the Congress the following year and thereafter. In the years that followed, Voronoff spoke at many other orthodox conferences, and had many followers and imitators in other orthodox medical circles. He had support from the French government; his writings were reviewed charitably in medical journals, and he published long, dull monographs on his work.

Voronoff's love of publicity can certainly be criticised. But it does not amount to quackery: indeed he may simply have been touting for more fee-paying patients. Ostentation was his major weakness and was to ruin him in the end. But in the context of the later nineteenth and early twentieth century, such use of publicity was not unusual:

the lives and activities of many famous surgeons, even in Britain, were the subject of considerable interest to the Press. Alexis Carrel also encouraged the attentions of journalists and understood their need for simple, dramatic stories of scientific breakthroughs. Voronoff's comments to the press showed a similar understanding of their needs; he was masterly in his use of the newspapers at a time when the reporting of science in Europe was strikingly naive. But Voronoff was wrong in his claims *and* made himself conspicuous: this, in the end, destroyed him.

IV

For about two years, from 1925–7, little was heard of Voronoff's sheep experiment in Algeria. But this work was progressing and had continuing aid from the Algerian Government Breeding Department. Two veterinary surgeons, M. Barlette and M. Boisselet, had done the routine work of grafting and were making the follow-up measurements on the sheep. Voronoff made visits from time to time and was noticed by a novelist, R.V.C. Bodley, who described the surgeon as 'a curious man, living a great deal for effect, and staging his experiments with the draft of an impresario'. Bodley also commented on Voronoff's 'devilish' appearance. This is not obvious in other depictions of Voronoff: Bodley may have had in mind the legend of Faust, with Voronoff playing the role of the Devil to his patients and sheep, offering them immortality.

The sheep experiment was a long-term one, and Voronoff was now looking closely at the offsprings of the grafted rams. Voronoff reviewed progress one year after the experiment started in 1926, and he announced that he was delighted with the results. He told the 1926 Congress of the French Association for the Advancement of Science that not only did gland transplants improve breeding and wool growth in the recipient sheep, but that these beneficial results were transmitted to the young animals born of the grafted parent. As a result of his important and significant conclusions, Voronoff suggested to a conference in Budapest in 1927 that the human race might be treated in the same way. He suggested that bright children might be gland-grafted early in life and so be endowed with even greater physical and mental powers. 'I call,' he said, 'for children of genius. Give me such children, and I will create a new super-race of men of genius.'

Voronoff had gone too far. This tasteless suggestion brought rebukes from the leader writers of many newspapers. At a British Association for the Advancement of Science meeting, the Bishop of Ripon's Sunday sermon called for a year's 'scientific holiday' from such medical research. The *Newcastle Evening Chronicle* agreed that scientists had to accept social responsibilities:

But although it is neither possible nor desirable to stem the tide of legitimate knowledge, there are certainly some avenues of advancement that are best left unexplored, and which, instead of adding to the sum total of human happiness, could only have a retrograde effect upon progress. In such a category are the ambitions of Professor Voronoff, of monkey gland fame, who at the Medical Congress just concluded at Budapest, called for children – the offspring of genius – so that by experimentation with his treatment he could produce a super-race of men. Hitherto his methods have been used only to restore life to the fading faculties of the aged, but now he is fired by the prospect of applying them to children of exceptional gifts, believing that by intermarrying they would create a wonderful new type of mankind.

The *Daily Sketch* of 13 September also called for a halt to genetic tinkering:

Science has achieved many marvels, but the soaring ambition of some scientists is apt to o'erreach itself. . . This Voronoff plea shows how liable is science, when divorced from philosophy, to outrage common sense . . . The scientist is too intent upon finding out, or proving something, to ask himself whether what he is striving for is really worthwhile.

These were probably the first ever calls for a moratorium and for social responsibility in scientific research: apart from the Nazis, no one, it seemed, wanted to breed a race of super-men.

Dr Hadwen, the watchful editor of the *Abolitionist*, was enraged. Hadwen was more concerned for the monkey donors, and complained that 'The idea of every human being being provided with an attendant monkey from which to patch himself up as occasion suggests, is one of the fine fruits of vivisectionist teaching, which should disgust every normal healthy-minded person.'

Voronoff seems never to have proceeded with his proposal to gland-graft young children, but he remained convinced of the

correctness of his approach. Perhaps his new experiments on producing such super-sheep diverted him from human work. The idea
that his grafts could permanently alter the genetic make-up of the
animals was an important claim. If Voronoff knew that he was
getting into deep and treacherous scientific waters, he made no
acknowledgement of it. Never profound in his writings, he was
perhaps even unaware of the seriousness of this new claim. It is also
clear that he entirely believed his findings. He welcomed investigation, and he was glad shortly afterwards when governments
throughout Europe investigated his claims to have permanently
altered the genetic make-up of the sheep.

Voronoff's risky, and eventually fatal, claim to have demonstrated
the inheritance of characteristics acquired during life was one of
many similar claims made in the 1920s, according to which, evolution on Darwin's model was wrong, and other forces were at work.
Darwin had suggested that changes in the environment selected the
fittest or best adapted offsprings; his critics, and the followers of
Lamark, believed instead that useful characteristics acquired during
life could be passed on to the next generation. To use Lamark's own
example, the long neck and front legs of the giraffe had resulted from
constant stretching up to reach food, whereas Darwin instead
suggested that giraffes born with long necks and legs survived better.
Lamark had lived and worked before Darwin, and his rather com-
monsensical views had been overthrown by the Darwinians, who
substituted natural selection as the mechanism of evolution. The
revival of Lamarkian ideas in the twentieth century occurred most
actively in the USSR, where famous genetic experiments with
fruit trees by Michuran and experiments with wheat strains were
claimed as providing evidence for them. The wheat experiments
were simple: it was claimed that wheat grown in cold climates
became resistant to cold within a few generations. The Lamarkian
viewpoint became official policy in the Soviet Union; the Lamarkian
biologist Lysenko exercised considerable authority over biological
research, and received official backing and honours.

Outside the Soviet Union the debate was sporadically reopened
despite the fact that endless generations of rats had had their tails cut
off in the nineteenth century without producing tailless rats, and

although endless generations of human beings had from earliest times undergone traditional mutilations such as circumcision without producing lasting genetic effect. Two events in 1926 caused something of a stir. The Professor of Psychology at Harvard, William MacDougall, taught rats to escape through a maze; he then bred the trained rats and found that the offspring could escape faster from the maze. He was modest about the results, but was clear that they showed the inheritance of acquired characteristics. Only many years later was the flaw in the experiments demonstrated. All rats bred in a laboratory improve in their maze running with subsequent generations, whether or not their parents had been trained. MacDougall had left out this vital control group.

A scandal had surrounded the other Lamarkian claim of that year. Paul Kammerer, as mentioned earlier, had shown that midwife toads repeatedly bred to give a nuptial pad on the hands, permanently acquired this pad. On 7 August Dr G. K. Noble of the American Museum of Natural History, who had examined the one remaining preserved specimen, declared that the pigmented pad was a fake, and that Indian Ink had been injected into the pad to give the appearance of a horny black pad. Kammerer declared his innocence, claiming that the specimen must have been interfered with. Shortly afterwards, he accepted a position in the Soviet Union, which he admired, but committed suicide shortly before his departure.

As a result of these claims and controversies there was a good deal of interest in the subject of the inheritance of acquired characteristics, and of possible improvements in the human race. Voronoff was ready to enter the fray of Lamarkian controversy. One thing is certain: he did this innocently, and was probably unaware of the issues involved. Voronoff ideologically was not of the Left, and could not, as a rich Russian émigré Jew, have felt any ideological pressure on his work to conform, as he would had he been working in Russia. Nor was he likely to be lionised by the Soviets, as the Marxist Kammerer had been.

In stating that the offspring of his gland-grafted sheep also showed the improved wool production of their parents, Voronoff was making an important claim which had to be investigated. The results could not be ignored by veterinarians and by government agriculturalists. If the breeding and vitality of livestock could be improved by testis transplants, then Voronoff's method was of practical value. The matter was raised in Britain by a Parliamentary Question to the Minister of Agriculture in September 1927. It was a planned question, designed to allow an announcement by the Minister. The exchange, as reported in *The Times*, was:

Sir H. Brittain (Acton, U.) asked the Minister of Agriculture whether he had had brought to his notice any of the experiments of Dr Voronoff in grafting an extra gland on to livestock for the purpose of producing a finer and more vigorous type: and, if so, whether these experiments could be looked upon as successful and would receive attention from his Department.

Mr Guinness, Minister of Agriculture (Bury St. Edmunds) – I am aware of Dr Voronoff's work on gland-grafting and I have arranged with Dr Voronoff's concurrence, for a small commission of scientific men to examine and report upon the experimental work on sheep which has been carried out at the Government breeding station in Algeria. Owing to the bad season the visit of the commission has been postponed until October or November, when the grafted sheep will be available for examination.

The watchful Dr Hadwen was dismayed and almost defeated. In the *Abolitionist* he wrote:

Of all farm animals, sheep are, we believe, the most liable to discomfort, and continual frights and torment . . . the shearing, the dipping, the farm operations, and rituals of various kinds before they are happy to be turned into mutton. Experiments to try to produce a 'super' race of sheep are being conducted on a ranch near Algiers. Our farmers will, we hope, withstand as long as they can the imposition of a new operation upon their flocks.

v

The investigation was extended by invitations to other nations, and four delegates from France, two from Italy, four from Spain, one from Argentina and one from Czechoslovakia were assembled. They travelled together from London on 31 October 1927, arriving in Algeria four days later. Though the senior person on the delegation was Dr F.H.A. Marshall, F.R.S., Reader in Agricultural Physiology at the University of Cambridge, the report was later put together by Dr F.A.E. Crew, Director of the Animal Breeding Research

Department of the University of Edinburgh. Crew had the necessary background for such an enquiry. He had supervised work in Edinburgh which claimed success with testis-grafting in fowls, and he had also dabbled in some experiments in rats, which suggested the possibility of inheritance of acquired characteristics. Also on the delegation were Dr A. Walton of Cambridge and Dr W. C. Miller of Edinburgh. The group were probably open-minded in their attitude to Voronoff: certainly the matter was not assumed to be quackery. There is no hint of ridicule in the files of the Ministry.

On 4 November they attended an official reception given in Algiers by General Maynier, Governor of the Southern Territories. A lecture by Voronoff then followed, and he also handed out to the delegates a substantial document describing his entire exerience with gland-grafting work. Next day the group moved on to the Bou Ghellel farm, eighteen miles from Algiers, to see the bull Jacky. It was this rejuvenated bull that earlier had established Voronoff's reputation and links with Algeria.

The delegates were shown Jacky, but careful inspection and palpation failed to detect any graft remaining under the operation scar. Two cows in season were produced for the bull. The bull became sexually aroused but did not mount the females. The British report was charitable about this failure: 'This could not be regarded as a fair test for the bull, for he had been handled by some score enthusiastic but often unskilled hands, was hemmed in a ring of ardently debating and admiring people and controlled by the uncoordinated efforts of four Arab herdsmen.'

After visiting Jacky, the delegates travelled south to the State Sheep Farm at Tadmit in Southern Algeria, a journey of 274 difficult miles into semi-desert. Here attempts to improve the indigenous sheep stock had been proceeding for many years by conventional selective breeding. These efforts had mostly failed, and the flocks were still very mixed in origin and of poor quality.

At the farm the testis-grafting experiment was explained to the visitors by M. Trouette, Director of Algerian Livestock Breeding in Algiers. The delegates were then shown the animals involved in the experiments – the grafted and non-grafted rams, and the offspring of these animals. The grafted animals were certainly healthier and heavier, and the delegates weighed some of the animals for themselves.

However, the British delegation, led by Dr F.A.E. Crew of Edinburgh, was disappointed at the absence of detailed records of the breeding performances. They also had reservations about Voronoff. In his confidential report to the British Ministry of Agriculture, Crew described the events at the farewell dinner which followed and at which Voronoff presided. It provides one of the few first-hand accounts we have of Voronoff. While it is critical of him, it is also sympathetic to the inner drive affecting the elegant French surgeon, then in his sixty-fourth year.

After the dinner one member of each delegation was invited by Voronoff to comment on what they had seen. Invited to dinner on the edge of the Sahara, and far from home, it seemed hardly the moment to criticise their charismatic host. Crew recounted his dilemma:

> The British delegate who was called upon to speak manifestly found it somewhat embarrassing to state that only when further evidence had been examined and further consideration given could he and his colleagues join in this anthem of thanksgiving . . .
>
> As time passed it became clear that Dr Voronoff, believing in himself and in his method, sincerely desires to make his contribution to human welfare, but that his almost religious fervour is blinding him to the necessity of establishing a scientific principle firmly before urging its incorporation into the business of life.
>
> Dr Voronoff is a man of very considerable charm with a fine dramatic instinct. This in itself makes it somewhat difficult for a British scientist to disentangle the originality which Voronoff undoubtedly possesses from the somewhat heroic enjoyment of the results which he describes.

But such was the hypnotic power of Voronoff's personality that a testimonial to him and his work was circulated at the dinner and signed by all his guests.

The delegates departed from Algeria and reached London on 12 November. Meanwhile, Voronoff characteristically had issued a press statement, full of his usual optimism and confidence. It was released before the delegates arrived home and pre-empted their considered verdict. *The Times* reported the events thus:

'SUPER-SHEEP'
Dr Voronoff's experiments
ALGIERS, Nov. 10 — Dr Voronoff, the gland-grafting scientist, claims to have produced 'super-sheep'.

The results of his experiments with sheep on the State sheep farm at Tadmit, Southern Algeria, have just been successfully demonstrated by Dr Voronoff to an international mission of agricultural experts delegated by the British, Argentine, Italian, Spanish and Czechoslovak Governments. Grafted sheep were observed to have gained 10 kilograms (22 lb) in flesh and 700 grams (1 lb 8½ oz) in wool, compared with ungrafted sheep. The first generation born of grafted sheep show a gain per head of 7 kilograms (15 lb 7 oz) of flesh and 500 grams (1 lb 2 oz) of wool, the latter being of a staple three inches longer compared with ungrafted sheep.

It is calculated that 100 grafted rams can assure the birth per annum of 5,000 'super sheep', giving 35,000 kilograms (31 tons) of flesh and 2,500 kilograms (5,500 lb) of wool more than the same number of ordinary sheep could supply. The mission expressed the opinion that the creation of a stud of grafted rams might profitably be introduced in all sheep-producing countries. – *Reuter*.

VI

It is clear that Voronoff was optimistic about the eventual outcome as the delegates returned home to make their reports. Every report but one was enthusiastic. In particular, the French and Spanish verdicts were favourable and their reports simply rehashed the material given to the delegates in Voronoff's handout. The Spanish delegation encouraged their Ministerio de Fomento to follow Voronoff's work. The French visitors must have found themselves in a difficult position when considering their verdict on Voronoff's experiments. His work and theories had been publicly patronised and supported by the Governor-General of Algeria and the local veterinary authorities; moreover, the French academic veterinary world had also supported Voronoff and, in Paris, had used his methods in animal grafting. Voronoff's post at the government-funded Collège de France made him almost a public employee, and his work was not unimportant to colonial policy. There must have been considerable pressure to support his Algerian work, particularly when it was under scrutiny by other governments, and the French delegation may have been picked with care.

Of the three delegates, none had impressive research records. The first was Professor M. Moussu, an academic veterinarian, from the École Nationale Vétérinaire at Alfort. He was accompanied by veterinary colleagues from Montpellier and from the breeding station in Tunisia. These men were to be criticised by others later. A fourth delegate was a more political representative: M. Carougeau, 'Inspecteur Général Divisionnaire Conseiller Technique au Ministère des Colonies' – the General Veterinary Inspector of the Colonial Ministry. The veterinarians had to report to the Ministry of Agriculture, but Carougeau reported to the Economic Minister at the Colonial Ministry, which suggests that the French government was watching the affair closely.

Moussu's report to the Ministry of Agriculture could not have caused any concern. His analysis was superficial and his attitude deferential and credulous. He believed everything he had been told and had few reservations about the conduct of the experiments. Of Jacky, the grafted bull, he said that 'Rejuvenation is obvious'; of the sheep, he reported that 'testis grafting stimulates functions of nutrition and increase growth in a very marked fashion.' He made no comment on the experimental design. The grafted animals they were shown were certainly more virile than the ungrafted: but the question was not whether the grafted and non-grafted groups were different, but how the experiment had been set up and conducted, since it was essential that the control group should have been randomly selected. To quibble about this would have involved criticising not only his veterinary colleagues, but also Voronoff and the government of French Algeria. Moussu perhaps took on trust what had not been shown to them.

The second French report was written by M. Carougeau. If Moussu had been enthusiastic, Carougeau was ecstatic. Voronoff's discoveries had been entirely confirmed – 'TOUTE ÉCLATANTE', he wrote in capitals: 'Algeria will be first to benefit,' he rejoiced, and the case of Jacky the bull was 'une magnifique leçon'. The Spanish report was similar to the French, and went on to recommend the use of Voronoff's methods in improving the Spanish sheep-rearing industry.

VII

Only the British report, written by Dr Crew in Edinburgh, was
unenthusiastic, and the others on the British delegation supported
his conclusions. The report was eventually published jointly by the
Ministry of Agriculture and Fisheries and the Board of Agriculture
for Scotland. Its conclusions were deliberately inconclusive: the
delegation were unable to conclude that there was clear evidence of a
revival of breeding in old rams, nor a transmitted increase in potency
to the next generation. They did not doubt that the animals shown to
them supported Voronoff's conclusions, but they would have liked
other assurances. The report seemed optimistic about the eventual
success of testis transplantation, but the experiments they had been
shown were not adequate proof: 'Definite and detailed information
concerning the numbers involved, or of the pedigree and relation-
ships of the individuals exhibited was not forthcoming. Moreover the
sheep were not confined under proper experimental conditions, nutri-
tional factors were disregarded, and control was unsatisfactory.'

The report pointed out that the sheep used were of very mixed
stock, deriving from earlier attempts to improve the flocks by the
addition of imported animals. They had not been shown all the
animals, and the way the groups had been separated at first was
important in numerous ways. The number of types of sheep in each
group was vital. Even the method of dividing the sheep into experimental and grafted groups was important. It should have been
done at random – otherwise a stronger group might have been
chosen for grafting, or the measurement might have been biased.
The report was also curious about another point – the excluded
'graft failures', mentioned in an aside by Voronoff. If some grafted
animals had been discounted as failures, did this not mean that the
weakest animals had been left out, inevitably leaving the heavier
ones in which the experiment had 'worked', or given the desired
result?

The main question to be asked, however, was how the flock had
been divided into the two groups initially. Unless a true, random
method of allocation was used, it would have been possible for the

enthusiastic experimenters unconsciously to pick out a potentially stronger group of young sheep for gland grafting, and so get the desired result. This may have happened: this, plus the exclusion of the weaker grafted animals, may explain how the grafted group, and their offsprings, were heavier and showed a better wool growth. If this happened, then the offspring of this group of animals would certainly be naturally stronger and heavier.

In addition the report had some pointed remarks to make about Voronoff's claims to have revived the vigour of Jacky the prize bull. The report unkindly suggested that Jacky may have been in poor health before the transplant operation, and may have revived spontaneously afterwards, so explaining the apparent rejuvenation. The report also remarked that the operation had been done in the spring, and that bulls become frisky towards summer. Moreover, Jacky's fertility after the gland graft was challenged in the report – 'there is a vague suggestion of doubt as to the paternity of some of his calves.' Lastly, the delegates had examined Jacky and they could not feel a graft remaining under the scrotal scar.

Quick publication of the report in Britain was authorised in view of public interest in the matter. Voronoff was given a copy of the critical report, and wrote to the Minister in London to complain. He felt understandably aggrieved, since the other delegations had produced favourable verdicts, and he enclosed a copy of the French report with his letter. But the British Ministry was not inclined to change its mind.

Dr Crew still wondered whether Voronoff might not be right, though his experiments were poor, and he repeated Voronoff's experiments with sheep. He concluded that there was 'a temporary stimulus . . . and a subsequent slowing down of activity', according to the *Edinburgh Evening News* of December 1929. Crew also received a rather odd letter from an obscure French veterinary scientist who was working not in Algeria, but in French Morocco. The writer was Henri Velu, the director of the breeding station near Casablanca, and he too had been grafting sheep. He had not been invited to Algeria. As a result of his own work, he could not confirm Voronoff's experiments. Moreover, he was critical of the way in which the Algerian experiments had been carried out. Velu's letter to Crew criticised Voronoff, and praised the British delegation's scientific detachment. Velu later became a persistent critic of Voronoff, presenting and publishing negative results of gland-grafting. By contradicting the French authorities, Velu invited personal criticism and, as we shall see, even attracted abuse from the French veterinary establishment.

The *British Medical Journal* also welcomed the British government report. The journal now called for caution, hoping that its readers had a short memory and had forgotten its earlier enthusiastic reviews of Voronoff's books: 'The claims made by Dr Serge Voronoff have had a wide and often uncritical publicity in the popular and agricultural press . . . In view of the unsatisfactory state of the evidence in animals, it would probably be unwise to conclude that grafting of testicular material in man . . . is definitely advantageous; rather should it still be regarded as *sub judice*.'

The *Lancet*, proudly pointing out that it had been sceptical about Voronoff for years, was also critical of the Algerian venture.

VIII

It may have been as a result of the official rebuff from the British Government that Voronoff decided to visit Britain. The ostensible reason for his visit was to accept an invitation to speak to the Cambridge Medical Society; but perhaps he arranged the visit reluctantly, and only did so to make his methods better known in Britain and to try to neutralise the Ministry's adverse comments. He knew that on such a trip to Britain he would be exposed to other opponents of his methods. This vocal British anti-Voronoff lobby was an odd coalition of anti-vivisectionists, eugenicists and race-horse owners, plus some informed sceptics. The anti-vivisectionists were more concerned with the fate of the monkey donors than with any benefit to Voronoff's human patients, while the eugenicists were obsessed with the possibility that Voronoff might poison the human stock with monkey characteristics: the objections of the race-horse owners will be dealt with later. Ironically, all groups agreed on one thing – that gland-grafting worked, and hence had to be opposed. In making this assumption, they encouraged and aided the wide acceptance of gland-grafting.

Voronoff reached London on 20 May 1928. His original plan had been to use the new aeroplane service, but his plane had to turn back to Paris. Instead, he and his secretary travelled by road and sea; his chauffeur and the Rolls Royce had gone on ahead, but on this occasion Voronoff's West African valet did not accompany them. In London, he stayed in a luxurious first-floor suite at the Savoy Hotel, while his staff had small rooms on the top floor. He made numerous visits to the theatre, but in spite of this, his English did not improve. He had a number of social engagements, including lunch with the Duke of Westminster; later in the trip, Voronoff rejuvenated the Duke's decrepit Scotch terrier.

A more public engagement was a dinner given in London on 24 May by a wealthy colliery owner, Sir Henry Norman, a man of affairs who had held a number of public offices, and the guest list was published in *The Times*. Norman's interest in Voronoff is unknown, but the reasons for the presence of some of the other guests are more easily understood. They included George Bernard Shaw, who had always taken an interest in medical matters; he was a frequent visitor to Almroth Wright's Vaccination Department at St Mary's Hospital in London, and he used his medical knowledge in his works. Shaw disliked Darwinism, and Voronoff's Lamarkism may have appealed to him. Also at the dinner was Sir William Bragg, the Nobel Prize winner and future President of the Royal Society, while British biological science was further represented by Dr Peter Chalmers Mitchell, Secretary to the Zoological Society of London, who earlier had translated Metchnikoff's speculative work on prevention of ageing.

Of all those who sat down to dinner, the most closely involved with the French surgeon was Sir William Joynson-Hicks, then Home Secretary, and later Lord Brentford. As Home Secretary, he had responsibility for animal experimentation. Britain was almost alone in the world in requiring all animal experiments to be licensed by the government. Joynson-Hicks could grant or refuse a licence to Voronoff to operate on monkeys in Britain; hence he could prevent Voronoff from treating patients. There is evidence that Voronoff intended to obtain such permission, and that Joynson-Hicks was being lobbied by anti-vivisectionists and others to prevent Voronoff operating in Britain. No doubt the Home Secretary was glad of a chance to meet and speak with Voronoff personally, but the charismatic surgeon failed to charm this tough politician.

Voronoff went on to lecture at Cambridge. The committee of the student society must have been pleased that five hundred people turned up to listen to the gland-grafter. Voronoff gave a professional performance, and illustrated the talk with a film of his operation: it was one of the first surgical films his audience had seen. His lecture was translated as he went along by his young English-born secretary. Those who recall the occasion remember that the attitude to Voronoff was that he was a pioneer, although a controversial one. Next day there was a brief account in the papers but no criticism of the lecture. Indeed, a letter to *The Times* from Dr John H. Hannan of the Middlesex Hospital, who had attended the lecture, concluded that 'although virility can be undoubtedly obtained by gland-grafting, the problem of lowered resistance to disease associated with old age still eludes us.'

On the same day, the *Daily News* reported that a small group of Harley Street surgeons would soon start doing the operation. The criticism which was soon to shower on Voronoff during this visit did not question the success of the operation, but was directed at the use of monkeys, and the question of whether the operation might not be *too* successful, and poison the human race.

The anti-vivisection movement had always been strong in Britain, and had been responsible for tough laws against the use of animals for research or other use. Anti-vivisectionists made sure that Voronoff could not work in Britain. On 14 June, Mr Briant, the M.P. for Lambeth, asked in a Parliamentary Question whether Voronoff could carry out monkey gland transplants in Britain, and the Home Secretary, Joynson-Hicks, replied in person at Question Time about the man he met at dinner. He was brief and to the point. Perhaps because he had a major speech to make a few minutes later on the controversial new Church of England Prayer Book, or perhaps because he sensed an anti-Voronoff mood in the House, he was even more abrupt in replying to a number of anxious supplementary questions about Voronoff and his monkey gland transplants. Such anxiety had apparently brought together city radical M.Ps. and rural blimpish conservatives in opposing Voronoff. The exchanges were recorded in *The Times* next day:

Sir W. Joynson-Hicks informed Mr Briant (Lambeth N.L.) that Dr Voronoff was given leave to land in the United Kingdom on May 22 and no time limit was imposed. His object was to give certain lectures at Cambridge University and elsewhere, but no licence of any kind had been given him to experiment in this country.

Mr Briant asked if Dr Voronoff could operate experiments without a licence. The British public were extremely anxious to know that he should not have an opportunity of conducting dangerous and disgusting operations, which included the transfer of the organs of propagation from an ape to a woman.

Sir W. Joynson-Hicks – It is quite impossible that he should conduct any experiment involving vivisection or cutting operations on any animal without a licence and that licence I have not granted and do not propose to grant. (Cheers)

Lieut. Col. Fremantle (St. Albans U) asked if a human being was not an exception, and if he could not offer himself for experiment if he liked. Mr Radford (Salford SU) asked if it would be possible for some other licensed person to make an operation on an animal and to leave it to Dr Voronoff to complete the experiment on a human being. Did the Home Secretary not think that it was a violation of everything that was decent in our Constitution that this man should be allowed to conduct such experiments in this country?

Sir W. Joynson-Hicks – My hon. friend is really not right. No such experiments are conducted in this country at all and the suggestion that it will be possible to have an operator who has a licence will not work, because I am most careful to inquire into the nature of the operations conducted under a licence.

It seems likely that Voronoff did apply for a licence, and was turned down. Some years later he still had a grudge against the Home Secretary, by then elevated as Lord Brentford. Brentford died shortly afterwards, and Voronoff was insensitive enough to suggest that a monkey gland transplant would have prevented his early death. Voronoff made other attempts to operate in Britain and use monkeys, but gave up in the mid-1930s.

IX

The opposition in Britain to Voronoff continued. The anti-vivisectionists held a successful anti-Voronoff meeting in the Caxton

Hall, London, on 7 June, organised by the Duchess of Hamilton. Less expected was an attack on gland-grafting by Dean Inge from the pulpit of St Paul's. Voronoff was also criticised in the popular press and by pamphleteers. As we have seen, some of those who attacked him did so on the grounds that monkey characteristics might be transmitted from gland-grafted men to their children. One of Voronoff's noisiest assailants was a Dr M. Beddow Bayley, a general practitioner from London, who was at that time in the middle of a long series of pamphlets opposing vaccination – an opposition that was also shared by most anti-vivisectionists, since animals were used to produce the vaccine. Bailey wrote an anti-Voronoff pamphlet which had a brief introduction on 'Immunity' written by a Dr Edward Bach, a Harley Street bacteriologist, whose remit was to give the scientific background to Voronoff's monkey gland transplants. Bach clearly believed that such grafts worked; and would last for five or six years. Doubtless at Dr Bayley's prompting, he speculated on the effects of repeated monkey gland-grafting in one patient: 'The final result would be a harmonious settling down of the resultant species with vibrations and character-istics somewhere below the level of human and above that of the protein of the ape.'

This Harley Street rubbish was followed by Bayley's rambling polemic. But in it he exposed two contradictions in Voronoff's thesis. Voronoff claimed that his grafted parents would produce more virile offsprings: hence the possibility that monkey genes were transmitted was undeniable. Though Voronoff had denied this possible genetic disaster, his reassurances were unconvincing. Bayley's sharp mind also exposed another contradiction. It was being suggested by some that glands caused habitual criminality: but it was also being suggested that the glands of executed criminals should be used as donor tissue. If the testis could cause criminality, was it not out-rageous, demanded the pamphleteer, to use such organs for trans-plantation?

Another opponent of this 'bestial operation', as he called it, was Sir Kenneth MacKenzie, Bt., a Scottish landowner and man of affairs. Writing in *The Referee* of 3 June 1928, he felt that the medical profession was acting dangerously in allowing such monkey gland surgery to proceed in the absence of knowledge of the long-term effects. Like Bayley, he raised the spectre of ape-like children being born to grafted parents after gland-grafting. He was also concerned about the short-term effects on the patients themselves, fearing that the monkey testis graft 'will continue to secrete spermatozoa that will be carried through the body by the circulation. Is it "fantastic" to suppose that these sperm cells will have no effect on the psychic or moral condition of the patient: that those of a lower and *amoral* animal will not affect in some way those of the human being with which they mingle?'

But Voronoff had some dubious support from one of his companions at the dinner held earlier for him by Sir Henry Norman. Bernard Shaw wrote to the *Daily News* deploring the slurs put about regarding monkeys and said that it was about time that the human race was infused with some of the better characteristic of the simian race. He concluded that 'man will remain what he is in spite of all Dr Voronoff's efforts to make a respectable ape of him.'

It must have been an uncomfortable visit for Voronoff. There were, however, some compensations. Numerous patients consulted him and requested his operation: doubtless many of these travelled later to France for treatment.

x

After he had returned to Paris, Voronoff had a final but flattering rebuff from Britain from the third group who had criticised him: the Thoroughbred Breeders Association announced that they would refuse to put gland-grafted horses on the stud book. British horse-breeders had always maintained high standards and insisted on their records of breeding being beyond reproach. They had heard of Voronoff's attempts to prolong the breeding life of ageing European race horses by gland-grafting. As a result of the 'race purity' controversy surrounding Voronoff in Britain, the Association decided to act. The question of gland-grafted horses was raised at the Annual General Meeting. The discussion was serious-minded and, like the human monkey gland argument, centred on the possibility of genetic contamination of the recipient horse by a testicle graft from an inferior animal. The discussion mentioned that Voronoff had grafted the French horse Rabelais on 23 November 1928 at the Maison Laffitte. The animal died a few days later, but the gland transplant itself was not thought to have caused this. Other horses had been allegedly successfully grafted elsewhere, such as King Alfonso XIII's prize animal Inspirade, which had been operated on by the Spanish surgeon Francisco Lopez Cobos, who had been on the Spanish delegation visiting and assessing Voronoff's work in Algeria, and was an admirer of Voronoff.

The discussion at the Thoroughbred Breeders Annual General Meeting of 1928 was opened by Mr G. H. Drummond, a successful Northampton banker and horse breeder. He pointed out that, of necessity, only an inferior animal would be used as a donor for a testis graft to a prize animal: only a horse of small value could be spared for this purpose. Such a graft would therefore be a genetic danger to the blood stock. He was, he said, 'all for research to help nature: but when it went contrary to nature it could only lead to trouble.' Supporting Drummond was 'Professor' J. B. Robertson (the title was an honorary one), one of England's best known veterinary surgeons and certainly the greatest authority on horse breeding in the country. He was quite clear that genetically 'an animal, after being gland-grafted, was not the same animal as before.' Lastly, another distinguished Newmarket veterinarian, Professor Ernest B. Reynolds, spoke and confirmed that expert opinion suggested genetic dangers from the operation. After further discussion, it was unanimously agreed that the Association disapproved of gland-grafting, that a record of such grafted animals should be kept, and that they would not go into the stud book. Clearly, no one doubted that gland-grafting worked, or that the purity of breeding was in danger; and the Breeders Association's decision reinforced the idea that success in gland-grafting had been achieved.

XI

At the 1928 Austrian surgeons' meeting in Vienna, two papers were given in support of Voronoff's claims for his operation; and that year Dr Karl Doppler of Vienna invented a new rejuvenation operation which, he said, had been successful in two hundred cases, assessed independently. The operation involved exposing the spermatic cord from the testis and painting it with the irritant phenol. In this way, it was plausibly but wrongly claimed, the nerves to the blood vessels of the testis were damaged, the blood vessels relaxed and the increased blood supply revived testis function. The year ended with Voronoff's publication of another book. The English version was called *The Conquest of Life*, a title changed in later editions to the more down-market *How to Restore Youth and Live Longer*. It was translated by Dr G. Gibier Rambaud, who had held the post of Director of the Pasteur Institute, New York, who had been active in producing numerous gland extracts. It was intended as a popular exposition of Voronoff's works, and there was little new scientific material. Indeed his old, well-used 'before and after' photographs of transplanted goats and patients were used once more.

In America, Dr Morris Fishbein, editor of *Journal of the American Medical Association*, paused in his pursuit of Dr Brinkley to accuse Voronoff's book of deception and hypocrisy, and Fishbein made effective use of the British Algerian report. In Britain, the *New Statesman*, unaware of the report, cautiously welcomed the book and called it of first importance to agriculturalists. The *British Medical Journal* now felt it best to ignore the latest oeuvre of a man whom they had previously applauded. But the *Lancet* did review it, and by now probably felt vindicated in their earlier caution. After mentioning the unfavourable report of the British delegation to Algeria, the review continued thus:

It is doubtful, however, whether a book from an enthusiast concerning results which are still doubted by the majority of scientific men is to be welcomed . . . a popular exposition written in the vein of The Conquest of Life is somewhat premature . . . If, as the publisher's note puts it, it is meant to be 'a narrative of surprising interest, as gripping as a best seller and as full of surprises as a mystery story', then the author has achieved his object.

Such language is unusual in the bland book review pages of medical journals: the rebuke was a serious one.

VI
NEMESIS

In 1930, Voronoff was still highly regarded, and his operation was still popular. Patients still sought his services in substantial numbers: in the jargon of private surgical practice, he continued to be 'busy'. Also busy were a number of other private surgeons who still believed in the operation, though Voronoff managed to put it about that only he himself had the totally successful *méthode*; and some private veterinary surgeons were active who had made themselves rich not only by claiming to perk up prize breeding animals who had lost interest in making money for their owners, but also by operating on senile pets. For Voronoff there were also small domestic pleasures to add to the daily routine of the gland surgeon. In 1930, a sixty-year-old Australian surgeon had visited Voronoff to study his methods. He then had a gland graft. After the operation, the visitor fell in love with Voronoff's secretary and took her back with him as his wife, and started testis transplantation in Australia. This Australian surgeon's life and works are well enough known to serve as an example of the 'second generation' gland-grafters who studied under Voronoff, and who themselves had a brief celebrity even in the 1930s.

Henry Leighton-Jones was born in New South Wales in 1868 and practised as a dentist from 1859 onwards. He took a two-year medical course in Kentucky from 1898 to 1901, and one further year of study in Edinburgh gave him the 'triple qualification' of the Scottish Colleges of Physicians and Surgeons, which allowed him to work as a doctor in Australia. He eventually settled in Darwin, covering a large area with his energetic services.

In 1928, at the age of sixty, he retired. During his retirement he began the study of endocrinology and read Voronoff's publications on gland-grafting. Fired with this new enthusiasm, he travelled to Paris, learned the method, and returned home, where he built a monkey cage based on his own watertower, hiring a man to attend to the monkeys, which were obtained from the Sultan of Jahore. He added a new feature to the operation, blood-grouping the monkeys before use and matching them to the human patient. Other local practitioners acted as surgeon and anaesthetist to the monkey and, the work was carried out in a little private clinic in Morisset.

These testis grafts were carried on until the Second World War, when the Japanese invasion of Singapore interrupted the supply of donor monkeys. In the preceding decade, Jones is thought to have performed about thirty testicular grafts, four thyroid grafts and six ovary grafts. He died five weeks before his seventy-fifth birthday, shortly before he was due to give a paper reviewing his experience with grafting.

I

But in the wider world of endocrinology, the mood had turned against gland-grafting much earlier than this. At the International Congress of Physiology in Boston in 1929, at which Voronoff spoke on his usual theme of the success of gland-grafting, an event of great importance occurred. The paper which profoundly impressed the delegates was given by a Dr Funk, who announced that he had, at last, isolated a hormone from the testis gland. To do so had involved a major research project, and one which had needed considerable funds. Some money had come from McCormick, the Chicago meat millionaire, who had been interested in rejuvenation for years, and had undergone the Steinach operation in 1922. His wife had once discussed a partnership with Voronoff, and they had planned to open a rejuvenation clinic and beauty shop in Paris.

Now, forty-one years after Brown-Séquard had made his premature announcement of the extraction of an active testicular substance, a potent, convincing hormone was available. In castrated rats it restored weight and hair growth. Voronoff must have nervously awaited news of the other effects of the extract. Yes, said Funk, testosterone was being used for rejuvenation of the aged, and the first results were good.

For Voronoff, it must have been an exciting moment, but also one tinged with disappointment. His life's work had been based on the assumption that the testis was an endocrine gland, and that, in old age, gland-grafting could be beneficial. He had been ridiculed, yet now the hormone had been found. Voronoff could now see himself as a courageous pioneer who had used transplantation of the testis during the extraordinarily long period before the isolation of the male hormone from the testis had been accomplished. At the time of the Boston conference, Voronoff was sixty-five years old. He must have felt that his place as a pioneer in the history of science was secure, as the man who, in the uncertain early days of rejuvenation, courageously used imperfect transplantation methods until the pure testis hormone was available.

But if Voronoff was pleased that the testicular hormone had at last been discovered, the evaluation of the new hormone which followed was to give less dramatic news – destroying not only hopes of rejuvenation, but Voronoff's reputation as well. Extensive studies found that the hormone could restore some 'maleness' to castrated animals – in other words, restore the 'secondary sexual characteristics' – but it could not reverse ageing or sexual decline. The testis hormone – testosterone – could not rejuvenate: there was also increasing criticism of the results claimed for Voronoff's earlier testis transplants in humans and in sheep. Attempts to repeat his sheep experiments failed. The decline of testis transplantation was imminent, and in the 1930s nemesis followed the hubris of the 1920s.

Moreover, as the 1920s ended, there was a new seriousness in the western world and a new attitude towards youth. The frivolity and irresponsibility of 'modern youth' were condemned by clergy and leader-writers. The ageing survivors of the First World War could not cope with the behaviour of the new generation. There was no longer the same cult of youth: perhaps it was more than a coincidence that there was simultaneous disenchantment with gland-grafting.

II

At the very end of the decade Voronoff toured the world. In Persia he inspected some men claiming to be 140 years old. In November 1929 he lectured to the Ceylon Branch of the British Medical Association; the lecture was introduced and the lecturer praised by the local

President of the Society, Dr S. Muthah. By February, Voronoff had reached Madras in India. There he gland-grafted a local prince, Sir Sarapchand Hukumchand, aged fifty-seven, and ovary-grafted his wife, aged thirty-eight. A dignified protest at the use of monkeys as donors for these operations was made by the local Jain religious community, but in vain. From India, he travelled to South-East Asia. At press conferences on his travels he claimed that the French Government had sent him on a tour of their colonies to lecture on gland-grafting methods. As usual, he may have slightly misled the journalists, but not entirely. On the last leg of the journey he sailed from New York for Europe in August 1930, travelling on the liner *Paris*. On the journey home he had some interesting company. The young entertainer Maurice Chevalier was also returning to Paris after his success in America. During the voyage, the new star of the entertainment world no doubt joined the great gland surgeon for an *aperitif*. If so, Chevalier would have done well to study Voronoff's methods closely, for the surgeon had occupied the centre of the stage for ten years.

Voronoff was clearly in top form. Later that year, perhaps confident that the use of the new extracts of testis would vindicate his earlier work, he announced that he was giving up testis transplantation and would devote himself instead to cancer research.

This period of apparent success culminated in another happy event. Since the death of his second wife in 1921, Voronoff had remained unmarried; he now fell in love. In 1929 King Carol, the unpopular ruler of Romania, had visited his friend Voronoff at the Château Grimaldi. Accompanying the divorced King was his mistress, Mme Lupescu, and she brought with her Gertrude Schwartz, her 'cousin'. Gossip suggested that Gerti was the King's daughter born to Mme Lupescu. Gerti and Voronoff saw much of each other, and after his world tour, they were married in Bucharest. The King gave Voronoff a decoration to mark his services to medical science; Voronoff in turn gave lectures and performed some gland transplants. At the time of their marriage, Voronoff was sixty-five years old; Gerti was twenty-one, and very beautiful. Voronoff paid her many public compliments.

His assistant Dr Dartigues left him at this time, though the reasons for this are not known. Voronoff continued his work with the help of a new Roumanian assistant, Dr Alexandrescu, and carried out experimental transplantation of human cancers to monkeys. In 1932 he made claims that these tumours grew in the monkeys, and that he could 'cure' these growths. But by then no one was listening.

III

There was no clear point at which opinion turned against testis-grafting. A minority had always been sceptical and might have agreed with the anti-vivisectionist Dr Hadwen, who used to say that a grafted monkey gland was 'nothing more or less than a piece of dead meat put in the wrong place.' Those who had criticised the claims of the gland-grafters in the 1920s were not listened to, but they began to win the argument in the 1930s. Because there had been these critics in the 1920s, and because the monkey gland transplants were becoming increasingly embarrassing, the historical record was soon to be rewritten to suggest that there had been no orthodox support at all for rejuvenation by grafting.

Early criticisms of Voronoff were to be found in a small number of reports, starting in the mid-1920s, when surgeons at the Mayo Clinic repeated Alexis Carrel's study of kidney-grafting from one dog to another, and showed that these grafts eventually rejected. Scientific papers studying skin grafts from one human to another appeared in the journals, suggesting that rejection could occur frequently, and that young skin or blood grouped skin grafts fared no better.

An important contribution to the loss of faith in gland-grafting was made in 1925 by a short paper by R. G. Hoskins from the Laboratory of Physiology, Ohio State University, entitled 'Studies of Vigour IV: The effect of testicle grafts on spontaneous activity'. As mentioned earlier, Hoskins was the editor of the journal *Endocrinology*; at one time he had been enthusiastic about testis transplants, and had published in *Endocrinology* the study of the San Quentin testis transplants by Dr L. L. Stanley. Hoskins was well aware of the earlier history of such transplants, of which he gave a masterly and lengthy account in his 1925 paper. His experiments had been carefully undertaken, and may well have been the first truly objective study of the subject. His four-line conclusion at the end of a long paper was that testicular grafting was ineffective.

But these negative laboratory studies made little change in clinical practice: Voronoff and his method survived for some years to come. In the inter-war period, the gulf fixed between the laboratory and the hospital remained wide. The system of private practice which encouraged Voronoff protected him to the last. In the end the aftermath of Voronoff's Algerian experiments was to be a major factor in discrediting gland-grafting and its exponents. It is hardly flattering to European clinical science that the follies of human gland-grafting were largely exposed by veterinary surgeons.

The Britons who had joined the international delegation to investigate Voronoff's methods in Algeria were full-time veterinary academics, while Henri Velu, who correctly disproved the claims for testis transplantation, had a full-time salaried post in the Breeding Station in Morocco: the last people to want to stop gland-grafting were those surgeons and vets who made their living from private practice. Gland-grafting was poor science, but good business.

The British delegation to Algeria had not been impressed with Voronoff, his methods or his results. But they had not ruled out the possibility that he was right. They had called for further study of his claims for enhanced virility and wool growth, but little or nothing was done in Britain, and it was left to others to do this work. There was a suggestion that the Animal Breeding Unit in Edinburgh might set up such an experiment with government funds, but in the end only a few animals were grafted with little effect, and a large-scale study was not set up. Dr Crew concluded from these experiments that gland-grafting in sheep gave only a temporary result.

IV

The first major blow to Voronoff's reputation came with a report from Henri Velu, who had written to Crew in Edinburgh.

Henri Velu was a talented French veterinary surgeon who as a young man had been a prize-winner at the Alfort Veterinary School. He had settled in Morocco in 1912 and then founded the Breeding Station at d'Ain Djema. He published his scientific papers on gland-grafting in 1928 at the age of forty-one. His previous output of research had been substantial, consisting of sixty-one scientific papers of high quality. In them he had made considerable contributions to knowledge of the detection, incidence and prevention of disease in animals. In spite of his remote colonial base, he was increasingly well-known, and was to gain further honours later. We do not know when his gland-grafting experiments started, but it was certainly before the international group's visit to Algeria. It is likely that Velu would have heard earlier, via the newspapers, of Voronoff's claims for the improvement of sheep in Algeria, or it may be that Voronoff's support by the French Government and French veterinarians was well-known in his profession. He may have been initially cautious about Voronoff's claims: later, as a result of his own experiments, caution changed to disbelief in gland-grafting in general, and concern that Voronoff was damaging the reputation of French science.

Velu's experiments were carried out on a small number of sheep, but his methods were better than Voronoff's. He found no evidence that testis transplantation affected wool production or breeding, and, in addition, he carefully studied the fate of the grafts. A key ingredient in Voronoff's claims was that the graft, when examined under the microscope long after the operation, was allegedly present and active. Velu agreed that, in some animals, some tissue could remain at the site long after the grafting had taken place. He concluded, however, that the cells in this lump of tissue which remained were not those of the original graft, but had come from the host animal itself. The 'graft' was really a scar, plus some inflammatory cells. Velu's clear analysis of graft rejection is in accord with later knowledge, and his paper gives one of the first correct accounts of the microscopic features of graft rejection. He describes the rejection mechanism correctly – 'une zone d'invasion cellulaire massive'. He realised – again correctly – that these invading cells, which give the spurious appearance of a persisting graft, were the wandering cells of the body – 'les cellules migratices'. Later, he even refers to a 'spécificité foncière des individus' – a specific functioning of the individual. Velu then affirmed that such grafts are always rejected, and that death is always the rule: – 'la mort du tissu testiculaire transplanté est la règle.' Velu's views and even his terminology anticipated the assumptions and attitudes of transplantation immunology of twenty-five years later.

v

Velu courageously faced the French veterinary establishment at one of the regular meetings of the Académie Vétérinaire on 20 June 1929. This meeting took place about one year after the official investigation of Voronoff's sheep experiments, which had been investigated and exonerated by the French veterinary world and by the French government. In Velu's paper to the meeting the data on testis transplants was good, and his studies had none of the deficiencies of Voronoff's reports. He showed that testis transplantation was ineffective, and concluded his lecture with a peroration calling, in the name of Claude Bernard, for better French science. He ended provocatively, but justifiably, by calling the claims for testicle grafts 'une grande illusion'. Velu was a brave man to contradict the findings of the government-sponsored Algerian sheep experiment. Moreover, Professor Petit, head of the Veterinary School at Alfort, was present at the meeting. For ten years Petit had been a committed Voronoff supporter, and together they had done some lucrative gland-grafting of valuable race horses at Alfort. Petit doubtless had attended the meeting in order to defend Voronoff and support Professor Moussu, his veterinary colleague at Alfort, who had written the French report on the Algerian experiments. It may well be that Petit had prepared a dignified rebuttal of Velu's conclusions, but instead he attacked Velu personally. Perhaps he had been annoyed at Velu's characteristically blunt language and criticism. Velu, he said, was 'making himself a determined detractor of testicular grafting'. He had been 'deceived by his personal experiments, and has only given modest credit to the work of others, refusing to acknowledge that they had shown a physiological role of the grafts'. Petit went on to defend Professor Moussu, reminding the audience of Moussu's 'critical mind'. He finished by attacking Velu again – 'let us simply note that he has failed where others, more talented, have succeeded.'

Fortunately this attack seems to have had little effect, and Voronoff's claims were treated with increasing cynicism. Nor did it damage

Velu or his career in the long term, particularly now that his view was becoming generally accepted. He continued to write and speak on the ineffectiveness of testis transplantation, and by 1932 he had won the argument. In 1934 he was elected to the French Academy.

The Algerian sheep experiment had been a government project, and had been used as an example of successful colonial policy. It was last heard of in 1931 at the International Colonial Exhibition in Paris: at the Algerian stand, the old embarrassing claims for better wool production and increased weight of grafted sheep were made for the last time.

VI

Two other major studies of the gland-grafting of livestock had been undertaken, as a result of Voronoff's Algerian claims, both of which had the support of their governments. The first of these was in South Africa, and was sponsored by the department of the Director of Veterinary Services and Animal Industry. The second took place in Australia and was supported by three bodies – the Sheepbreeders Association of New South Wales, the Australian Government and the University of Sydney. It was carried out at the Veterinary Research Station, Glenfield, a publicly funded institution.

The South African report appeared in late 1930, and the Australian one in 1931. They reported similar findings. The Australian report was the most hard-hitting, and began by reviewing the 'extravagant claims made by various investigators'. Their conclusions from their own study were clear and simple: 'There is no good evidence here provided of any beneficial influence on body weight or wool production as a result of testicular grafting . . .'

In clinical practice, surgeons were now prepared to denounce the monkey gland transplants. Dr Frank Lahey of Boston told a meeting in Philadelphia that European surgeons had been wrong in claiming that successful grafts could be made using animal tissues. But he went on to support another false claim. Only human tissue grafts would succeed, he said, and then described three allegedly successful human-to-human parathyroid gland transplants. These could not have succeeded, and Lahey was wrong. In 1934 the Baltimore surgeon Harvey B. Stone made another erroneous claim, which was to reappear repeatedly in the literature until the 1980s – that if human gland tissue was grown in tissue culture, using the recipient serum for seven days, it could afterwards be transplanted with success into another human. It seemed as though surgeons could not abandon the dream of a successful gland transplant.

Some biologists were now getting interested in transplantation, and laboratory studies of the rejection of tissue grafts were eventually to bring some order into this muddled area. Leo Loeb in America spent a lifetime on such work, confirming that tissue slice grafts rejected, but he failed to analyse the mechanism correctly. Peter Gorer in Britain and George Snell in America began to lay the foundations of the new science of transplantation immunology. In the 1940s, as a result of Peter Medawar's work, it was agreed that the common type of grafts from one member of the same species to another always rejected. Grafts between different species, such as monkey to man, were even more rapidly rejected. A second monkey tissue graft to a human who had already rejected a monkey tissue graft would reject in a matter of hours.

VII

In Kansas, 'Dr' Brinkley's fortunes underwent a more obvious moment of crisis. While Voronoff's reputation suffered a steady erosion at the hands of immunologists and veterinarians, Brinkley was attacked and destroyed quite suddenly. He had been un-molested for about ten years after his ejection from Chicago in 1920. During this time he had built up his impressive private hospital, his powerful radio station, and a network of pharmaceutical franchises. Moreover, he had extended the use of his goat gland operation from patients simply undergoing physical and sexual decline to include others with prostatic problems. Perhaps he sensed the gathering opposition, even in the sticks, to gland-grafting for rejuvenation. To numerous prostatic sufferers he offered a safe and simple operation instead of the risky, conventional operation for removal of the prostate, which at that time had a high mortality rate.

By 1929, Brinkley had made some local enemies. He also found himself being investigated by journalists from the *Kansas City Star*.

This investigation may not have been impartial: the newspaper ran the WDAF radio station, which rivalled Brinkley's KFKB. Brinkley's suspect medical degrees were exposed, and the claims for his operations disputed. But Brinkley had friends as well, not least as a result of giving local politicians free time on his radio station. With their help, investigation of his methods and his misuse of the radio were delayed. But in the late 1920s a vigorous house-cleaning operation was being mounted by the American medical professional corporations. They were anxious to improve standards of medical education and licensure, and determined to revoke the medical degrees given by the 'diploma mills' and evanescent medical schools of early twentieth-century American medicine. Many of the medical men so qualified had served well the rough-and-ready needs of expanding America; many were skilful practitioners, and there were ways in which, even late in life, they could obtain qualifications to meet the new orthodoxy. Others had to give up medical practice and took up different work. Many took to the road, moving about America as the new regulations were slowly enforced, state by state, with Arkansas as the last haven for the old medical empirics. But Brinkley decided to stay in Kansas and fight.

The local State Board of Medical Registration and Examination eventually moved against Brinkley in 1929. Their complaint listed not only his unsatisfactory degrees but made accusations about his professional conduct, accusing him of felony and alcoholism. In addition, it stated that his expensive goat gland transplants were ineffective. These allegations were part of a broad, catch-all approach; it was clear that many of the complaints about his conduct involved single, isolated incidents, and many of these allegations could not be substantiated. The main thrust of the State Board's argument eventually fell back on attempts to discredit his medical qualifications and his practice of surgery.

Brinkley made a pre-emptive move to head off the danger from the Board and attempted to block the proposed action against him. In the District Court, and then in the Supreme Court of Kansas, he argued that the State Board had only quasi-judicial powers and could not deprive him of his livelihood. His argument failed. Judge Burch delivered the Kansas Supreme Court's opinion, and clearly enjoyed writing what must be one of the minor gems of legal and medical history:

The complaint [i.e. of the State Board] was by no means confined to challenge of the success of the licensee's goat gland operation, the claimed result of which is that dotards having desire without capability may cease to sorrow as do those without hope, and the complaint was not that the licensee is a quack of the common, vulgar type. Considered as a whole, the gravamen of the complaint is that, being an empiric without moral sense, and having acted according to the ethical standards of an imposter, the licensee has perfected and organised charlatanism until it is capable of preying on human weakness, ignorance and credulity to an extent quite beyond the invention of the humble mountebank . . .

We have here a complaint that, by virtue of a license obtained by fraud, the imposter holding it is fleecing the defective, the ailing, the gullible and the chronic medicine takers who are moved by suggestion and is scandalising the medical profession.

The Supreme Court made its ruling in June 1930, and the State Board of Medical Registration and Examination was quickly able to hold its proposed hearing against Brinkley, which began on 15 July in Topeka, the capital of Kansas. The hearings attracted considerable attention, not least because of the appearance of Brinkley's ex-patients, summoned by the defence, who testified to his skills and the success of his surgery. Outside the court room they did handstands for the attentive photographers.

The State Board, represented by the Attorney-General, had by no means an easy time pressing home their allegations. The evidence that Brinkley drank heavily and was abusive rested almost entirely on the testimony of one family, who were easily shown to be unreliable witnesses and to have a personal grudge against Brinkley. The allegations of Brinkley's profanity also failed: no one seemed to mind that he often said 'God-damn' on the radio.

The Board's attempt to discredit the goat gland operation fared a little better, and Brinkley had impressive defence counsel. They were aware of the surgical attitudes to testis transplantation in the 1920s, and were ready to show that gland transplants were part of the orthodoxy of the day. All the contemporary textbooks and monographs had been assembled in Court, including the works of Voronoff and Thorek. Using these, Brinkley's counsel managed to discredit testimony against gland transplants in general, and managed to ruffle the expert witnesses who had been summoned to say that goat gland transplants were not effective.

Thus when Professor Thomas Orr, Professor of Surgery in the University of Kansas, took the stand, he was shown the standard texts and he soon found himself admitting that gland-grafting might work. Orr had initially taken the moderate view that gland-grafting was only in the experimental stage:

Mr Ralston (for Brinkley): You do not mean to say that Voronoff's experiments or work are still in the experimental stage, do you?
Professor Orr: Yes.
Ralston: Don't you know that it has been adopted by all or nearly all of the prominent physicians and surgeons of this country?
Orr: I know that it hasn't been adopted by most . . .
Ralston: Take the first work you read. Dr Thorek of Chicago has adopted it, hasn't he?
Orr: I think he has.
Ralston: Performing it every day?
Orr: I couldn't tell you how frequently.

Having admitted that the glands transplanted from monkeys could work, and that young glands were better than old glands, the witnesses were led by Brinkley's counsel to concede that young goat gland transplants might also work.

Brinkley's testimony came last. He was composed, plausible and articulate. His introductory statement was professional and mentioned urbanely that his early gland surgery training included a visit to Europe to study gland-grafting, notably the methods of the swiss surgeon and thyroid gland expert, Emil Köcher. He also hinted that Thorek in Chicago was a friend. Brinkley's knowledge of anatomy was impressive, as was his familiarity with the literature of gland-grafting. Why did he not publish his results, he was asked by his counsel. Brinkley replied simply that he had attempted to do so, but the medical journals would not publish such novel findings.

However, Brinkley's impressive defence of his goat gland transplants did not save him. While the Board could not prove deficiencies in his personal conduct or even convincingly discredit his gland-graft surgery, Brinkley's claims to possess conventional medical qualifications were shown to be fraudulent. His medical licence was revoked: he could no longer practise medicine in Kansas.

VIII

Brinkley's response to these reverses was to take a bold new initiative. Had it succeeded, the history of medicine and politics in the American mid-west might have been different. In September 1930, two months after his licence to practise medicine had been taken from him, he ran for Governor of Kansas. It was an impulsive decision, and when he took it the deadline for candidacy was past. His only hope was to enter as a 'write in' candidate, whereby the voter is asked to write the name of the candidate under those names already printed in the ballot form. There is one major snag in this type of candidacy: the name written down must not only be spelt correctly, but it must have the correct initials added to it. Only 'J.R. Brinkley' would suffice as a valid vote.

Brinkley ran a remarkable campaign. His opponents were unimpressive products of the local party machines, and the rural mid-west voters sympathised with his exasperation with the authorities and big city bosses. Historians also credit Brinkley with the introduction into his campaign of many novelties which were to become routine thereafter – radio broadcasts, promotional literature, prerecorded messages and extensive use of aeroplane journeys to save time and impress the gatherings at the airstrips. Both his opponents were bachelors, and Brinkley's wife was always at his side. It was the height of the Depression and he had a sensible manifesto which proposed lower taxes, better roads, free textbooks, free road licences, and the creation of lakes throughout Kansas in an attempt to increase the rainfall. Many years afterwards, when Brinkley was dead, such lakes were dug; by a stroke of irony, one near Milford submerged the former site of his hospital.

The final result of this famous Kansas election, the announcement of which was delayed for many days because of the closeness of the vote, was

Henry H. Woodring	Democrat	217,171 votes
Frank Haucke	Republican	216,914 votes
Brinkley		183,278 votes

The margin of victory was small and Brinkley was not far behind the two leaders. In addition, there were up to 50,000 spoiled papers, which were almost certainly mostly votes for Brinkley, judged invalid because of small errors in the writing of his name. Many people still consider that Brinkley won the election. He also got thousands of votes in the simultaneous gubernatorial contests in neighbouring states where he was not a candidate, but which were reached by his radio broadcasts.

This was the height of Brinkley's fame. The 1920s had been a time of success; the 1930s were one of increasing frustration. Though he moved and built a new, more powerful radio station in Mexico, right on the American border, and had a moderate success in the 1932 campaign for Governor, the American government and medical establishment increasingly harassed him, and did so with growing success.

IX

Though Voronoff's sheep experiments had been discredited, and Brinkley's work was under a cloud, public disenchantment with human testicle transplantation was slow, as if many wanted to believe that rejuvenation was possible. Voronoff's entry in the 1926 *Encyclopaedia Britannica* on 'Rejuvenation' was repeated in a shortened form in the 1929 edition: only later was it removed. We do not know how many surgeons in the world practised testis transplantation in the 1920s, but dozens had visited Voronoff to learn the *méthode*. Professor André Marror of Turin performed over 200 such grafts, as did Professor Pende in the same city. A very large number of transplants were carried out by the Portuguese surgeon Alberto Madureira, and in Rio de Janeiro, Professor Richard Spiur and Castro Araujo were enthusiasts for the operation. Their moment of disenchantment is not known. Ivor Back at St George's Hospital in London is alleged to have done some monkey gland-grafting, but these were not routine, no doubt because of the difficulties in getting a licence for such animal work. We do not know when Kenneth Walker of the Royal Northern Hospital, London, stopped doing such surgery using human donor glands. By the end of the 1920s Max Thorek in Chicago was less sure than before of the success of gland-grafting and now stated that testicle-grafting was only suitable in selected cases. Dr Leo Stanley was still at San Quentin, but neither he nor the prison authorities seemed to have the old enthusiasm for the gland operation. There were no more statements to the press about those who had been grafted, even after the annual sports day. A few veterans kept up the old claims, probably because it meant good business. As late as 1934 the New York plastic surgeon Dr H. L. Hunt shifted to using pituitary gland transplant from animals in a pointless and almost fraudulent treatment for human dwarfs.

In later years, these surgeons had lapses of memory when surveying this part of their careers, as did their valedictory orators and their obituary writers. Dr Stanley retired from San Quentin in 1954 and the booklet put together to mark this occasion omits his pioneering of gland-grafting work. Ivor Back's obituary did not mention his enthusiasm for Voronoff's invention and even the obituaries which followed the death of Max Thorek in 1960, at the age of eighty, fail to record his ten-year obsession with testis transplantation. Kenneth Walker lived until the 1950s and by then had forgotten his own Hunterian Lecture of 1924, in which he described Voronoff's method with approval. In a book called *Commentary on Age*, published in 1952, he said that Voronoff's results were 'no better than the methods of witches and magicians'.

Of all those practising gland-grafting, no one was more reluctant to give up than those veterinarians in private practice who used the operation to revive old pets or prolong the breeding life of valuable stud animals. For them, gland-grafting was good business. As late as 1931, G. P. Mair, a veterinary surgeon in Reading, was still enthusiastic about the operation and published an account in the *Veterinary Record* of a long series of successful operations which included the revival of a sealyham bitch, a black retriever, a red pekingese, a fox terrier, two thoroughbred horses, and a prize boar.

x

There was a new and serious mood about in the 1930s after the extravagances of the 1920s. The disenchantment with attempts by surgery to tinker with the human body's normal processes reflected a new scepticism about the role of scientists and medical men. While in the 1920s many accepted that the miracle-workers in medicine and science could achieve great things and might be able to mould the human body, there was now disbelief that this could be achieved, or indeed that it was desirable. If man was malleable, perhaps he was best left alone. The literature of the time reflected the new mood. The scientific utopianism of the 1920s, which assumed that science could bring about a new order, gave place to the anti-utopian novels of the 1930s, notably Aldous Huxley's *Brave New World*. The first and earlier such novel had been the Russian work *We* by Eugen Zamyatin and described an authoritarian state – the Single State; compliance to the State was achieved by a surgical operation on the brain. By the 1930s the assumptions were that drugs would be used, and in Huxley's novel mass obedience was achieved by means of the Soma tablet. Such novels showed that those who could reshape mankind were not to be trusted.

Another group which had sought to change the human race were also in disarray by the 1930s. The eugenicists were on the defensive, since one major assumption in their position had been swept away – the claim that the stunted, sick, poorer classes were genetically inferior and hence a danger to others. This was shown to be untrue. Their deficiencies were not genetic or a matter of breeding, but resulted quite simply from their being underfed. In Scotland, John Boyd Orr gave milk to working-class schoolchildren and reported theatrically that 'they grew in front of my eyes'. The poorer classes could no longer be considered a genetic danger to the race. The eugenics movement was further demoralised in the 1930s when the Nazis acted on the assumption of the inferiority of some races and individuals, leading to sterilisation programmes and eventually the extermination of those considered unfit.

Brinkley's last years were difficult ones. As we have seen, after the discrediting of his rejuvenation operation he had diversified into the treatment of enlarged prostate glands, and the patients came in huge numbers. During this time he found the medical establishment increasingly hostile but he was protected by powerful political friends. Even in 1937, his income from his medical practice was $1.3 million. But in 1938 he made a mistake. One of his most persistent critics, Morris Fishbein, the editor of *Hygeia*, the journal of the

American Medical Association, called Brinkley 'a quack' in an article in the magazine. Brinkley sued for libel, and lost. His income dropped, and Texas – to which state he had moved – revoked his medical licence. Only Arkansas remained as a haven for irregular healers, and Brinkley moved his organisation to the capital, Little Rock. There he constructed a magnificent private clinic, and with the help of other medical men of dubious training, he offered diverse medical services. He continued to have an interest in politics, and became a vocal American isolationist and spokesman for right-wing organisations. But he was increasingly pursued by litigious ex-patients, with whom he preferred to settle out of court, rather than risk further damaging publicity. He may have paid out $1 million in this way: he also owed $0.5 million in back tax. With his income dropping, he decided to make himself technically bankrupt, having sensibly first made over all his goods to his wife.

He made a confident new start, but his health then gave way. In August 1941, he suffered thrombosis in the arteries of one leg. The leg was amputated by conventional medical men, and numerous complications followed. He had a long convalescence, and returned to Texas in poor health. On 26 May 1942, he had a heart attack and died at the age of fifty-six.

XI

But Voronoff survived and was to live on until 1951. However, patients seeking a new youth no longer consulted him. Not that the market for rejuvenation had disappeared: on the contrary, it has always been present, and always will be. The Steinach operation remained popular in the 1930s, and W. B. Yeats, the Irish poet, had the operation done in 1934, probably by the Harley Street specialist sexologist Norman Haire. In that year Haire published his book *Rejuvenation*, a popular work with optimistic themes, which claimed that the Steinach operation would, among many effects, lower blood pressure, improve digestion, increase energy and concentration and possibly increase sexual desire, potency and pleasure.

But Voronoff and Steinach had had their day. Instead there was a new star in the increasingly murky world of rejuvenation – Dr Niehans and his Swiss clinic for tissue therapy. Niehans became the world's premier rejuvenator in the 1930s and 1940s, reaching the pinnacle of his fame in 1953 when he was called in for consultation by Pope Pius XII.

Niehans had started as a gland-grafter in the seclusion of a Swiss private clinic. In 1927, when the importance of the pituitary gland as the controlling influence on the other endocrine glands had recently been realised, Niehans carried out pituitary transplants using calf or sheep donors and claimed to cure rheumatism and diabetes, and to stimulate the growth of dwarves. During a visit to America this last claim led him to be mobbed by persons of small stature.

As gland-grafting fell into disrepute in the 1930s, Niehans wisely diversified into the injection of cells rather than transplantation of slices of organs. He constructed a plausible scheme, based on the muddled early theories of endocrinology in the 1920s. He proposed that many human defects and diseases, including ageing, were the result of deficient secretion from the glands of the body.

Niehans was secretive about his treatment, but it is clear he used cells taken from the glands of unborn sheep from 1948 onwards. He took advantage of the widespread view at that time that young tissues would not reject, and his choice of the foetal sheep exploited the ancient appeal of the lamb as an animal conferring grace and perhaps spiritual healing. In fact, we know that the cells in his injections were destroyed within minutes of injection. They had no stores of any useful material and had nothing of value to release into the circulation.

Niehans had style. Like Voronoff, he created an aura of success. While Voronoff used a high profile to attract patients and confidently claimed success, Niehans used name-dropping and the mystery and secrecy of his work to establish his reputation. Many celebrities were open about their visits to him, and having once taken the treatment and paid dearly for it, the pressure on them to report success was considerable. Gloria Swanson and Somerset Maugham talked of their treatment and Noël Coward went for a short visit. It was rumoured that the Duke and Duchess of Windsor were patients, and Niehans's denials merely increased the gossip. Konrad Adenauer's denial that he had visited the clinic was probably true but was not believed. Niehans's announcement that he had turned down

Stravinsky for treatment demonstrated the Swiss rejuvenator's flair for publicity.

Niehans gained immense wealth and an international reputation through his treatment. In 1953, he was called in as a last resort by Pope Pius XII, then in chronic unexplained poor health and with a persistent hiccough. Tissue therapy was given after Niehans had brought two pregnant ewes to Rome from his clinic. The Holy Father allowed himself to be photographed with Niehans; as a result, Niehans was invited to join the Vatican's select group of scientists, the Pontifical Academy, which also included Sir Alexander Fleming. The controversial decision to invite Niehans was widely criticised and led to a new constitution being proposed for the Academy.

Niehans's only challenger was the veteran Soviet biologist Bogomolets, whose theories of ageing had official backing from 1930 onwards. Working in his own institute in Kiev, Bogomolets put forward a variant on Metchnikoff's earlier theory that the body's ageing connective tissue began to strangle the other cells of the body. Bogomolets prepared an 'anti-reticular cytotoxic serum' which, he claimed, dealt with the overactive connective tissue. The serum was supposed to rejuvenate, and was widely used in World War II to accelerate healing: it was also alleged to have anti-cancer properties. The serum was useless and its use has now been discontinued, but in the many Soviet gerontological research units and clinics other materials, such as procaine, are used to revive and restore the aged.

Though Voronoff was neglected in the 1930s, while Niehans was gaining this rich clientele, he courageously held to his original views, and published a number of dignified defences of his life's work. He often said that his critics were unable to obtain good results because they could not match his surgical method. Voronoff remained popular with publishers, and in his books he explored broader themes. Once again, he may have been imitating Alexis Carrel, whose book *Man the Unknown* had been immensely successful. But at least Voronoff did not share Carrel's gloomy preoccupation with what he saw as the continuing moral and physical degeneration of the human race, as a result of which he came to believe that eugenic measures were essential, and sterilisation necessary. This elitist attitude led Carrel to admire Nazi authoritarianism, and he settled in German-occupied Paris, where he was provided with a research institute. He died a few days after the Liberation.

Voronoff's works are instead testimonies to freedom, individuality and love. The first of Voronoff's later works was on animal behaviour. *Love and Thought in Animals and Man* (1937) was a kindly book based on his observations in his monkey colony. In 1947, he published *From Cretin to Genius*, a series of essays on the creative process and the early struggles of artists and scientists, including his own. In his next work *The Sources of Life* (1943) he returned to the old familiar ground again, and in a dull book simply repeated the old arguments and reprinted his dated 'before and after' rejuvenation pictures and the drawings of the now discredited microscopic evidence for survival of his grafts. All three books sold well, and were translated into a number of languages. His last work was almost his most extraordinary – *Les Groupes Sanguines chez les Singes: La Greffe du Cancer Humain aux Singes*. It dealt with his human cancer work, in which he claimed to have successfully grafted human tumours to monkeys using blood group matching. He then claimed to have cured the cancer growing in the monkeys.

When World War II broke out, Voronoff was on a lecture tour in South America, where he still had a sympathetic following. He decided to return quickly to the Château Grimaldi, and was briefly in the public eye again. It was quite like old times. Embarking by boat for France, the seasoned publicist announced to newspaper men that the French government had invited him to return to set up a special hospital in Cannes for the war wounded. If this had been a serious plan it had to be quickly abandoned. Italy declared war on France and there were brief hostilities between the two countries along the Riviera. Voronoff's château was expropriated by the Italians, and he fled west by car via Spain to Portugal. He was in good company. Many of the rich, leisured inhabitants of the South of France, like the Duke of Windsor, also took the same route to escape from the Axis armies. From Portugal, Voronoff sailed to America, and took up citizenship as one of the Russian quota of immigrants. He had escaped the dangers of being a Jew in occupied France. His two brothers remaining in Paris were arrested by the Nazis: they were never seen again. His third brother, Alexandre, who worked at the Château Grimaldi, also disappeared in this way. His fourth brother, in Russia, may have suffered the same fate.

At the end of the war, Voronoff and his wife returned to France. They found that his château on the Riviera had been destroyed in the fighting at the French-Italian border. He was now eighty years old. Increasingly frail and deaf, he and his wife settled to live quietly in the Hôtel du Louvre in Paris. There are some hints that he now faced litigation from patients who considered that they had contracted serious diseases from the transplanted monkey testicles. Certainly he had taken that risk.

XII

By creating new problems of burns both in pilots and civilians, the war had turned the attention of serious scientists to the problem of the survival of grafts between human beings. If skin grafts could survive when transplanted from one person to another, then these burns could be treated. Careful new studies were undertaken, most importantly by Peter Medawar, and at last a clear and authoritative answer emerged to the problem of the survival of grafts: skin grafts between all persons except twins always rejected. At about this time, skin grafting was used in a legal case to prove that two boys who had been separated at birth were identical twins. They accepted skin grafts from each other, and the law now recognised that this could only happen in twins. In the year of Voronoff's death, a small number of human kidney transplants were carried out in an attempt to treat patients dying of kidney failure. No drug treatment was available and these grafts also invariably rejected, but it was the start of a new and successful era.

Voronoff died in 1951. He had fallen during a visit to Lausanne and broken a leg. During his convalescence, he developed a fatal chest complaint – perhaps pneumonia, or perhaps a clot passed from his legs to the lungs. There were few obituaries to mark the event; his death was ignored by the conventional medical journals and was noted only briefly by the newspapers which had followed his early career so intently. The *New York Times*, unaware of their earlier interest in him, not only misspelt his name, but concluded that 'few took his claims seriously'. But *France Illustrée*, in a generous valediction, concluded that he had simply lived too long in a changing, younger world: 'Voronoff, décédé à Lausanne à quatre-vingt-cinq ans, était venu trop âgé dans un monde jeune.'

To the sophisticated new generation of surgeons and immunologists now studying the invariable and seemingly insuperable biological barrier to successful transplantation, it seemed incredible that anyone could have believed in the past that the rejection problem did not exist. It was now fashionable to ridicule those who believed earlier that skin and other grafts from one person to another who was not a twin could succeed.

For Voronoff, the monkey-gland transplanter, a very special hilarity was reserved. It was, and is, a superficial judgement.

POSTSCRIPT

'I do hope,' said Dr Alex Comfort darkly, 'that you're not going to spend too much time writing on these gland-transplant people. You'll spread the false impression that the attempt to retard ageing is peopled exclusively with quacks.'

Patrick M. McGrady, *The Youth Doctors*, 1968

The history of science, like the history of all human ideas, is a history of irresponsible dreams, of obstinacy, or error. But science is one of the few human activities – perhaps the only one – in which errors are systematically criticised and fairly often, in time, corrected . . .

Karl Popper, *Conjectures and Refutations*, 1963

It is usual to think that medicine and science progress in straight lines. Conventional descriptions of scientific advance suggest an orderly unveiling of the mysteries of nature by means of the infallible 'scientific method'. This comfortable view has been increasingly criticised by philosophers and historians. The straight lines in which science apparently progresses are drawn only retrospectively, and many ideas, seemingly supported by convincing results, are abandoned without comment, although they may have been widely believed. Most of these erroneous ideas, which do not appear on the lines of progress, are simply forgotten and the people involved totally or partly ignored. But a more serious fate awaits those innovators whose ideas are later shown to be seriously in error – and in particular those who, like Voronoff, sought publicity and public approval for their advances. The workers are easily ridiculed later, and major deviations from what is perceived as the line of progress may even carry accusations of deception or even quackery.

Voronoff's use of monkeys' glands to restore youth contained a comic element from the start, and when events later discredited this approach, ridicule was easy. The allegations of quackery are also easily made. In *The Youth Doctors*, an otherwise charitable account of man's endless hunt for rejuvenation, Patrick M. McGrady unkindly concluded that Voronoff 'turned the noble struggle for ageing retardation into a garish freak show.'

I hope that this book has shown that the usual dismissive verdict of history on Voronoff, and the monkey gland era, is unjustified. The events show that he was widely believed and copied and had a place in conventional medical science of the day, and he was not alone in his methods of transplantation. Nor was he even the pioneer of gland grafting. But his weakness for publicity, and his persistent advocacy of testis transplantation, made him conspicuous at the time, and still more so when later work showed the impossibility of inter-species transplants. As a result of the new sophistication, it was easy to scoff at Voronoff and his faulty methods. The reasons for this self-deception are complex, and are at the centre of the story, but all his actions suggest a sincere belief in his claims for success. From 1919 onwards he consistently reported benefits to his human patients from testis transplantation, and even when, ten years later, the rest of the scientific world began to ridicule it, he courageously continued to affirm his belief in his operation. A quack would have shifted his ground and diversified his interests when the mood changed.

Much else does not justify the label of quackery. He was not itinerant, but worked most of his days in Paris. He had conventional medical posts and a conventional training: he attended conventional conferences, at which his papers were accepted for presentation. He had stable relations with colleagues and assistants. There was a stream of visitors to his clinic, where they were made welcome and were enthusiastically shown his *méthode*.

As to the question of his motivation, it is obvious that Voronoff did not need money: he was already independently rich. But one particular feature of Voronoff's career is enough to refute the suggestion of quackery – the fact that he was fifty-three years old, and at the height of a conventional career, when he started human gland-grafting. Until then he had never veered from orthodox methods or ideas. He was a well-established medical man, past middle age, and so wealthy that he need never have worked again, who attempted vigorously and late in his career to give his new discovery to the world. His motivation was clear: he was a man with a mission, and wished to be remembered, almost as if he wished to be young again intellectually. His creative mind had produced an idea which fitted the needs of the times and which if true was of fundamental significance. To dismiss him as a quack, however, involves a distortion of the history of science. It suggests that the orthodox scientific and medical community was incapable of such error. Moreover, it suggests that such episodes are rare and unusual or occurred before the modern period. Instead, it is much more helpful to regard the monkey gland era as one of the delusions which from time to time beguile the scientific community. To re-evaluate Voronoff and his work in this way makes more sense of the events.

Voronoff certainly lacked awareness of the traps involved in scientific research, and his writings lack profundity. His eclectic scheme of biology drew on Carrel, Huxley and Lamark. But his error was simply self-deception, and this defect he shared with many scientists before and after him. He was almost alone in grappling with the problems and others failed to take an interest in transplantation, or to check his results. Writers on scientific method concentrate on the methods of successful practitioners; an occasional look at those who failed can be just as rewarding. Voronoff had no difficulty in producing new ideas, but he lacked a sceptical assessment of them, nor did he design experiments to disprove these hypotheses. His failing was a defect of refutation, not of creativity. Had his ideas been correct, and his methods still poor, he would have remained famous.

Voronoff did not fail to produce noble hypotheses. Indeed, as he pointed out in his own writings, scientists share with great artists this capacity for creativity. Voronoff was wrong, but we can now restore him, as a flawed scientist, to within the broader scientific community.

In two small matters he was a pioneer. The use of monkey tissues is now becoming respectable. In the mid-1980s, methods of preventing rejection had become powerful enough for respectable transplant surgeons to turn once more to the monkey as a source of donor organs. In 1984 a baboon heart was transplanted to a human baby, and the graft lasted longer than was expected. Perhaps, as methods improve, monkey and animal tissue will again make up the shortage of organs for human transplantation. Voronoff may still be remembered as the first to grapple with the problems involved in the regular supply and use of such donors. And, if nothing else, Voronoff was first to launch the debate and face the criticism involved in the regular use of animals as tissue donors for human transplants.

SOURCES AND
BIBLIOGRAPHY

Unless otherwise stated, the source used for this book has been the *New York Times*, and the many entries on Voronoff were reached through its Index. The early history of attempts at rejuvenation are given in the general works listed above, notably Eric J. Trimmer, *Rejuvenation* (London, 1967). Brown-Séquard's life and works, and the subsequent history of testis extracts, are given in Merriley Borell, 'Organotherapy, British Physiology and the Discovery of the Internal Secretions', *Journal of the History of Biology* 9, 235–268 (1976), 'Brown-Séquard's organotherapy', *Bulletin of the History of Medicine* 50, 309–320 and in Diana Long Hall, 'The Critic and the Advocate: Contrasting British Views of the State of Endocrinology in the Early 1920s', *Journal of the History of Biology* 9, 269–285 (1976).

The rejuvenators of the 1920s and 1930s are described rather uncritically in a number of books: Norman Haire, *Rejuvenation: The Work of Steinach, Voronoff and Others* (London: George Allen and Unwin, 1924); Eric J. Trimmer, *Rejuvenation: the History of an Idea* (London, Robert Hale, 1967): Kenneth M. Walker, *Commentary on Age* (London: Jonathan Cape, 1952). A slightly better analysis is given in Patrick M. McGrady Jr., *The Youth Doctors* (London: Arthur Barker, 1969). These works have fairly good bibliographies. For a revisionist account see R. E. Billingham and W. B. Neaves, 'Paratransplantation and tissue therapy', *Perspectives in Biology and Medicine* 22, 320–332 (1979). The scientific papers on testis transplantation are all found in Michael F. A. Woodruff, *The Transplantation of Tissues and Organs* (Springfield, Illinois: Charles C. Thomas, 1960).

Regrettably, Voronoff's personal papers and correspondence have not survived, nor are there any good biographical studies of him. His life is described briefly and badly in Hector Ghilini, *Le Secret du Dr Voronoff* (Paris: 1926) and by Max Thorek in *A Surgeon's World* (Philadelphia: Lippincott, 1943). In spite of these difficulties other sources are good enough to have enabled a reasonable account of his life to be constructed.

The correspondence between Voronoff and Carrel is found in the Alexis Carrel Collection of Georgetown University, Washington D.C.

Other incidents are recorded in the watchful anti-vivisectionist journal the *Abolitionist*, published by the British Anti-Vivisection Society. Clinical medical journals in the 1920s carry reviews of Voronoff's books and his works. Voronoff was admired by the popular press and many articles about him can be traced through the International Index to Periodicals.

The gland-grafter's conventional scientific papers are found in sources such as Woodruff *supra*, but in addition, Voronoff had a remarkable output of monographs and books, starting with his early conventional surgical texts. His output of books seems to have peaked in the Thirties, when his reputation was declining. Voronoff continued to be popular with publishers in Paris and New York until the 1940s.

A complete list of his considerable output of books and monographs can be found in the Catalogue de la Bibliothèque Nationale and the National Union Catalog. Voronoff usually published first in French and translations into other languages might follow. Confusingly, some of his books had the title changed after translation, and a down-market edition might also follow bearing yet another title.

Voronoff's works are: *Essai sur les Trèves Morbides* (Paris: 1893); *Feuillets de Chirurgie et de Gynécologie* (Paris: Doin, 1910); *Traité des Greffes humaines: greffes osseuses et articulaires* (Paris: Doin, 1916); *Vivre* (Paris: B. Grasset, 1920), translated as *Life: a Study of the Means of Restoring Vital Energy and Prolonging Life* (New York: E. P. Dutton, 1920), translated by Evelyn Bostwick Voronoff (Madame Voronoff).

Copies of the lecture never given by Voronoff but printed in advance for the Congrès Français de Chirurgie have survived and the Library of Congress has the English translation also prepared in advance – *Testicular Grafts: Communication Addressed to the 31st French Congress of Surgery in Paris, October 1922* (Paris: 1922).

Greffes Testiculaires (Paris: Doin, 1923); *Quarante-trois Greffes du Singe à l'Homme* (Paris: Doin, 1924), later issued as *Rejuvenation by grafting* (London: G. Allen and Unwin, 1925), translated by Fred Imianintoff; and later reissued as *The Study of Old Age and My Method of Rejuvenation*, translated by Fred Imianintoff (London: The Gill Publishing Co, 1926).

Les Sources de la Vie, (Paris: Fasquelle, 1932) was translated as *The Sources of Life* (Boston: B. Humphries, and Toronto: Rierson Press, 1943).

La Conquête de la Vie (Paris: Fasquelle, 1933) was translated as *The Conquest of Life* (New York: Brentano's, 1928) translated by G. Gibier Rambaud, and was also reissued as *How to Restore Youth and Live Longer; L'amour et la pensée chez les bêtes et chez l'gens* (Paris: Fasquelle, 1936) and translated as *Love and Thought in Animals and Men* (London: Methuen, 1937). *La Greffe Testiculaire du Singe à l'Homme* (with G. Alexandrescu) (Paris: Doin, 1930).

Greffes des Glandes Endocrines: la méthode, la technique, les résultats (Paris: Doin, 1939), published in an English translation (London: Brentano's).

Du Cretin au Génie (Paris: Fasquelle, 1946) and New York: Edition Maison Français, 1941) was translated as *From Cretin to Genius* (New York: Alliance Book Corporation, 1941). A revised edition was published in Paris in 1950.

Les Sources Renouvelées de la Vie (New York: Brentano's, 1942).

Les Groupes Sanguines chez les Singes: La Greffe du Cancer Humain aux Singes (Paris: Doin, 1949).

La durée de la greffe des glandes endocrines (Paris: Doin, 1948).

The scientific papers given by Voronoff and Retterer at the International

Congress of Surgery are given in the *British Medical Journal*, Vol ii 121–124 (21 July 1923). The papers given to the International Physiology Congress are in the *British Medical Journal*, Vol ii 201–203 (1923).

Further biographical details on Voronoff are found in *Chanteclair*, No 59 p. 7 (1910). His wartime bone-grafting work is given a laudatory account in *Scientific American Monthly*, pp 307–309 (April 1920). The politics of Voronoff's appointment to the Collège de France are described in the Archives Nationale files F/1//26400.

Alexis Carrel's life is described in Theodore T. Malinin, *Surgery and Life; the Extraordinary Career of Alexis Carrel* (New York: Harcourt Brace Jovanovich, 1979). The Carrel-Voronoff letters are held in the Alexis Carrel Collection at Georgetown University Library, Washington, DC.

Though Voronoff's life and works have been neglected, Brinkley's career has received considerable study, notably in Gerald Carson's excellent book *The Roughish World of Doctor Brinkley* (New York: Rinehart, 1960). I have studied most of the sources used by Carson, and have added newer, unpublished material held in the Kansas State Historical Society, Topeka, notably Brinkley's personal papers gifted by his widow, and the transcript of Brinkley's appearance before the Kansas State Board of Medical Registration. The historic judgement given in the pre-hearing is given in *Kansas Reports* 130, 874–884.

Other sources on Brinkley are the ghosted biography by Clement Wood, *The Life of a Man: a biography of John R. Brinkley* (Kansas City: 1934); Sydney B. Flower, *The Goat Gland Transplant as originated and successfully performed by J. R. Brinkley ...* (Chicago: New Thought Book Department, 1921); Morris Fishbein, *A History of the American Medical Association 1847–1947* (Philadelphia: 1947) pp 503–516; Jack D. Walker, 'The goat-gland surgeon: the story of the late John R. Brinkley', *Journal of the Kansas Medical Society* 57 749–755 (1956); and Albert J. Schneider, "That troublesome old cocklebur": John R. Brinkley and the medical profession of Arkansas 1937–1942', *Arkansas Historical Quarterly* 35 27–46 (1976).

For a contemporary critical account of organotherapy see Swale Vincent, 'The present state of organotherapy', *Lancet* i (1923) 130–132. For uncritical accounts see G. A. Stockwell, 'Historical, critical and scientific aspects of Brown-Séquard's discovery – the so-called "elixir",' *The Therapeutic Gazette* 5, 812–19 and 6, 14–19.

See also Albert Schneider, 'The so-called rejuvenation treatment', *Medical Review of Reviews* 34 49–74 (1928); Armstrong Perry, 'The renewal of Youth by Surgery', *The Forum*; Eugene K. Illyin, 'Serge Voronoff', *World Review* 19–22 (1951), Nicolas and Lillian Kopeloff, 'Glands: facts vs fiction', *The New Republic*, 209–212 (19 July 1922), and Pan S. Codellas, 'Rejuvenations and satyricons of yesterday', *Annals of Medical History* 510–520 (1930).

The experience of other surgeons in gland-grafting comes from other scattered sources. Thorek gives a candid account of his early enthusiasm for gland-grafting in his autobiography *A Surgeon's World* and in his conventional scientific papers, notably that presented at Rome in 1923 and published as 'Experimental investigations of the role of the Leydig, seminiferous and Sertoli cells and effects of testicular transplantation', *Endocrinology* 8, 61–90 (1924), and in 'The present status of male sex gland transplantation', *Medical Review of Reviews* 29, 62–66 (1923).

Lydston's undoubted early involvement in testis transplantation is described in an obituary in *American Journal of Clinical Medicine*, 30, 234–235 (1923), and he published his early work in a series of articles, the most important being in *Journal of American Medical Association* 66 1540–43 (1916). One of the minor transplanters, H. L. Hunt, described his work in *Endocrinology* 6 652–654 (1922). Stanley's transplants are described by him as 'Experiences in testicular transplantation', *California State Journal of Medicine* 18, 251–253 (1920), and in a poor paper, 'Analysis of one thousand testicular substance implants,' *Endocrinology* 6, 787–794 (1922). A short biography of him is found in *The Centaur of Alpha Kappa Kappa* 1–9 (May 1951).

The suspect work of the Vienna Vivarium group has never been described in detail, though Arthur Koestler has defended one of the scientists – Kammerer – in his book *The Case of the Midwife Toad* (London: Hutchinson, 1971). Paul Kammerer's own praise for Steinach is found in Kammerer's book *Rejuvenation and the Prologation of Human Efficiency* (London: 1924).

For the influence of eugenics see Donald K. Pickens, *Eugenics and the Progressives* (Vanderbilt University, 1968) and E. J. Smith, *Race Regeneration* (London: 1918). Myths about masturbation are explored in Arthur N. Gilbert 'Doctor, patient and onanist disease in the nineteenth century', *Journal of the History of Medicine* 8, 217–234 (1975).

The British government's file covering the investigation of Voronoff's Algerian experiments are given in the Ministry of Agriculture file MAF 33/676, which contains useful background material, and copies of the Spanish and French reports. Voronoff's visit to Britain in 1928 merited a number of mentions in the *The Times*. The attack by M. Beddow Bayley in *Medical World*, 20 July 1928, has a useful list of articles published on the occasion of Voronoff's visit.

The debate among the horse breeders is given in *Report of the Twelfth Annual General Meeting of the Thoroughbred Breeders Association* (1928).

The destruction of Voronoff's reputation by Henri Velu was the result of a number of articles, but Velu's main conclusions are given in a forceful article 'État actuel de nos connaissances sur la greffe testiculaire', *La Presse Medicale* (1931), 39, 1496–98 (1931). For the continuing enthusiasm for gland-grafting in the veterinary world, see R. M. C. Gunn and H. R. Seddon, 'Testicular grafts on rams', *Veterinary Record* 11, 494–499 and the *Lancet*, 1299–1300 (1931). See also G. P. Mair, 'Gland-grafting and its economic value', *Veterinary Record* 11 484–493 (1931). Paul Niehans' own work is described in *Cellular Therapy from the Viewpoint of Doctor and Patient* (Thun, Switzerland: Otto Verlag, 1964).

Yeats's rejuvenation operation has recently attracted attention: see Stephen Lock '"O that I were young again": Yeats and the Steinach operation,' *British Medical Journal* 287, 1983 and Richard Ellmann, *Yeats's Second Puberty*, *The New York Review of Books*, 9 May 1985. See also Steinach E., Loboel, J. (ed), *Sex and Life* (London: Faber and Faber, 1940).

The allegations that Voronoff's grafts transmitted disease comes from Niehans and is reported by Patrick McGrady Jr in *The Youth Doctors*, p. 58.

INDEX